Engaging Students in Science Investigation Using GRC

Brett Moulding

Kenneth Huff

Wil van der Veen

Engaging Students in Science Investigation Using GRC: Science Instruction Consistent with the Framework and NGSS

Printed in the United States of America
First Printing: 2020

Photo credits: Dr. Michael Dahlby, Jacob Huff, Kenneth Huff, and Brett Moulding. Additional photos on Unsplash from Aaron Burden on the back cover and pages 16, 53.

ISBN: 978-0-9990674-3-7

ELM Tree Publishing
elmtree.publish@gmail.com
www.TeachingScienceisPhenomenal.com

Preferred Citation:

Moulding, B., Huff, K., & van der Veen, W. (2020). *Engaging students in science investigation using GRC: Science instruction consistent with the NRC Framework and NGSS.* ELM Tree Publishing: Ogden, UT. SBN: 978-0-9990674-3-7

Preface

Teachers play a key role in engaging students in science by creating a learning environment that piques curiosity and provides a structure for immersing learners in science performances to make sense of phenomena. Engaging students in relevant and interesting phenomena builds student curiosity, interest, and identity with science. Structuring learning to engage students in three-dimensional performance sequences helps students to apply science learning beyond the classroom.

A Framework for K-12 Science Education (*Framework*), Next Generation Science Standards (*NGSS*), and state standards based on the *Framework* describe science learning expectations in terms of three-dimensions of science - practices, core ideas, and crosscutting concepts. In this book, the reader is introduced to the science performance sequence of Gather, Reason, and Communicate Reasoning (GRC). This instructional sequence is an effective approach to facilitating three-dimensional student science performances. This book also provides teachers of science with specific guidance and examples for how to improve science teaching and learning consistent with the vision for science education presented in the *Framework*, *NGSS*, and three-dimensional science standards.

Collectively the authors of this book have been involved in science education for decades. They have been and are classroom teachers, professional development providers, science researchers, district and state leaders in state agencies and science teacher organizations, and members of numerous national committees on science education including - the National Research Council (NRC) *Framework* committee, *NGSS* writing team, writers of the National Academies of Sciences, Engineering, and Medicine report Investigation and Design at the Center, and many other National Academies reports. Based on this extensive experience, we believe the GRC instructional sequence is the most effective way to engage and support students in taking ownership of their learning and helping teachers to realize the new vision for science education that puts students at the center of scientific investigation. The GRC instructional sequence helps teachers organize instruction to engage students in making sense of relevant phenomena. The sequence of gathering information and data, reasoning about the meaning of the data, and communicating that reasoning through artifacts increases student interest and conceptual understanding of science. We have been formally using the GRC instructional sequence with teachers in professional development and classrooms for over 10 years.

This book translates research on teaching and learning from the *Framework* into an actionable structure for science instruction. This matters because the interactions between teacher and student ultimately determine the quality of student learning. Teachers are professionals and continue to grow and learn throughout their careers. As professionals, teachers engage in professional learning to develop the skills, knowledge, and dispositions to make decisions informed by research into how students learn. Teachers know what is best for their students. The GRC instructional sequence provides a structure for instruction consistent with the research on how students learn science.

Engaging Students in Science Investigations

We have worked with teachers across the nation in professional learning settings to develop and maintain a GRC lesson resource to use accompanying this book. This resource is a website with vetted GRC lessons for each K-12 grade-level and *NGSS* standard. The website is *Going3DwithGRC* and can be found at https://sites.google.com/3d-grcscience.org/going3d.

In addition to the hundreds of GRC three-dimensional lessons, you will find lesson templates, information on how to choose appropriate phenomena, and elementary and secondary matrices for science and engineering practices and crosscutting concepts. We are excited to share the GRC instructional sequence and resources and hope you will find this approach to teaching and learning valuable. Enjoy the journey.

We would like to acknowledge the assistance of Dr. Lindsay Beddes, Dr. Louise Moulding, and Stacey van der Veen for reviewing, editing, and production of this book. We also acknowledge the professional teachers who have informed this book during professional development, lesson development, and feedback. Students are the ultimate consumer of the work that we do and we acknowledge the role they play in motivating this text.

Brett Moulding
Kenneth Huff
Wil van der Veen

About the Authors

Brett Moulding was a science teacher for 20 years and state science specialist in Utah for 15 years. He is  currently the director of the Partnership for Effective Science Teaching and Learning. He is a former member of the National Academies Board on Science Education. He was a member of the committee that developed *A Framework for K-12 Science Education: Practices, Crosscutting Concepts, and Core Ideas* and a lead writer for the *Next Generation Science Standards* writing committee. Recently, Brett served as the co-director for the committee that wrote the National Academies of Sciences, Engineering, and Medicine report *Science and Engineering for Grades 6-12: Investigation and Design at the Center.*

Kenneth L. Huff is a middle school teacher in the Williamsville Central School District in New York. He  has 28 years of science teaching experience and is a National Board-Certified Teacher in early adolescent science. Early in his career, he founded a Young Astronaut Council which he continues to lead for fifth through eighth-grade students at his school. In addition to his teaching responsibilities, Kenneth is the President of the Science Teachers Association of New York State. He served as a member of the writing team for the *Next Generation Science Standards*, a member of the Board of Directors of the National Science Teaching Association, and President of the Association of Presidential Awardees in Science Teaching. Kenneth has been recognized for his teaching and science leadership including receiving the Presidential Award for Excellence in Mathematics and Science Teaching, the Empire State Excellence in Teaching Award, and has been elected as a Fellow of the American Association for the Advancement of Science.

Dr. Wil van der Veen is the director of the Science Education Institute at Raritan Valley Community Col-  lege. He has designed and facilitated hundreds of professional development experiences to support effective science teaching and learning and has lead over a dozen state-wide and national science education programs, including many programs to support the implementation of the *Next Generation Science Standards*. In collaboration with Rider and Princeton University, he started the NGSS Teacher Leader Program to identify and support science education leadership within school districts. Prior to his involvement in education, Dr. van der Veen was an astronomy research scientist for 20 years. During this time he published more than 50 science research papers in addition to over 20 articles on science education. He has been recognized for his teacher professional development and science education leadership including receiving the Astronomical Society of the Pacific's Thomas J. Brennan Award for outstanding contributions to the teaching of astronomy in grades 9-12; he was also a two time recipient of the New Jersey Science Teachers Association Petix Award for extraordinary support and contributions to NJSTA.

Contents

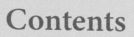

Chapter 1

Phenomena and
Student Science Performances

SCIENCE is the human endeavor of developing explanations for the causes of phenomena. Science explanations are supported with empirical evidence from data, observations, and existing science laws, principles, or theories. Explanations establish the causal relationships for phenomena, while arguments provide the logical reasoning for how each line of evidence supports an explanation. Science phenomena are the everyday events we see around us, such as clouds forming, billowing, and disappearing. Phenomena include less frequent events such as clouds forming in rows, waves, anvil shapes, having flat bottoms, or banner shapes streaming from mountain tops. We encounter hundreds of phenomena in our daily lives. Phenomena have causes and we can use science to construct explanations for the causes of each phenomenon. Science explanations are supported by empirical evidence – this is what distinguishes science from other ways of knowing. Moulding and Bybee (2017) assert that it is important for students to understand why science phenomena are at the center of science instruction and how science is distinguished from other ways of knowing.

> Throughout this book, we use the term phenomena. This refers to naturally occurring science phenomena as well as human-engineered phenomena.

Students engage in making sense of phenomena by developing questions, collecting and analyzing data, generating and utilizing evidence, and developing models to support explanations and solutions. This process leads to a stronger conceptual understanding of science content. Students build more meaningful science understanding by engaging in investigations that are relevant and meaningful to them. Engaging all students in science requires significant effort on the part of the teacher to develop meaningful learning experiences.

Teachers can nurture curiosity and motivate student learning by choosing phenomena that are locally and/or culturally relevant. Selecting relevant phenomena builds students' interest in science.

Relevant learning experiences pique students' curiosity and lead to greater identity with science (National Academies of Science, Engineering, and Medicine; NASEM, 2019). This approach can build on students' natural human inquisitiveness and support learners in developing a useful understanding of how science works beyond the classroom. Locally and culturally relevant phenomena help promote the participation of all students and support language development for English language learners. A community-based context for science learning generates useful language and facilitates communication skills as students apply their learning beyond the classroom. Science learning is enhanced when connections are made to familiar contexts and built on students' prior knowledge (NASEM, 2018).

> *Throughout this book, we use the expression "making sense of phenomena." This refers to students connecting the explanations for a phenomenon to their existing schema of core ideas, crosscutting concepts, similar phenomena, and personal experiences.*

When students try to make sense of a phenomenon, they may not have an explanation, but they can use their senses to experience the phenomenon and accurately describe their observations. The teacher's role is to foster student learning by organizing a series of performances that guide the learner's reasoning. In meaningful performance sequences, students use a suite of practices, relevant crosscutting concepts, and multiple core ideas to construct causal explanations. The performance sequence we recommend and promote throughout this book is the Gather, Reason, and Communicate Reasoning (GRC) sequence. GRC begins when students gather data, concepts, and ideas to reason the causes of phenomena and then communicate this reasoning. GRC is both a performance sequence for students and an instructional sequence for teachers. This book focuses on ways to engage students with phenomena to learn science consistent with the vision of A Framework for K-12 Science Education (*Framework*), the Next Generation Science Standards (*NGSS*) and state standards consistent with the *Framework*.

> *Making sense of phenomena is the process by which students construct meaning and usable knowledge that becomes more comprehensive and sophisticated over time.*

Using Phenomena to Initiate Science Instruction

Our use of "student science performances" in this book refers to the active engagement of learners in making sense of phenomena. These performances include physical as well as mental engagement and the implied hands-on investigation of phenomena.

A significant new direction for science education is the shift from giving students information to helping students develop skills and knowledge to use information. Information is readily available with the push of a button or a verbal request to a hand-held electronic device. "The world no longer cares about what you know; the world only cares about what you can do with what you know" (Dr. Tony Wagner,

Harvard University's Innovation Lab). Our role as educators is to prepare students to use available information to make sense of the natural and engineered world. This requires a shift in what we value in education: a shift from learning about to constructing meaning about phenomena. New three-dimensional science standards call on teachers to help their students develop skills in evidence-based argumentation through activities that bring out students' initial ideas about science phenomena while allowing them to be confronted with opposing ideas and evidence to trigger conceptual growth (NASEM, 2018). This requires teachers to engage students with relevant phenomena that lead to student-constructed explanations for the causes of phenomena. The goal is for students to apply their science learning beyond the classroom.

Science education should engage students in wondering about the phenomena they observe in the world and developing empirical evidence to support explanations for the causes of those phenomena (Figure 1.1). Students are surrounded by phenomena in their daily lives and curiosity can lead to an interest in developing explanations.

Figure 1.1 Examples of Phenomena Students May Encounter in Their Daily Lives

- In a dark room, we can't see the color of the objects.
- An alarm clock sounds louder when it is closer.
- Some birds sing in the morning and others sing at night.
- Moisture forms on the outside of a glass with ice water.
- The lights in a traffic signal have three distinctly different colors.
- Bees make a buzzing sound when they fly, but moths do not.
- Not all grass is the same color of green.

Engaging students in learning about science via phenomena increase their understanding of how the world works (NASEM, 2018). Teachers foster student curiosity by presenting phenomena that spark student questions and drive teaching and learning. The teacher's role in the classroom becomes transformed into a facilitator of student reasoning as students plan and carry out investigations. A key role of the teacher, therefore, is to create coherence in learning, where students build upon prior knowledge and develop evidence-based explanations for the causes of phenomena.

As students investigate one phenomenon, they acquire new scientific knowledge they apply to explain other novel phenomena. Phenomena are the focus of our scientific curiosity and they should be front and center in science classrooms beginning in the lowest grades and continuing through a student's entire science education. As students engage with phenomena, they need (and will maintain) curiosity, creativity, and a healthy dose of doubt, important ingredients to be innovative in the 21st century.

Phenomena can be introduced to students in many ways; however, it is best when done in a manner that captures student interest. Fostering student curiosity is paramount to having students become interested in learning science. It is important that phenomena are presented in a way that causes students to develop their own questions. We have found success by presenting phenomena as observations, not as essential questions or an explanation of the observation. It is the student's job to develop questions with a purpose toward constructing an explanation for the causes of the phenomena. Below are some useful examples of effective ways to introduce phenomena focused on the Earth-moon system.

- Tell a story to describe a phenomenon. "When we were camping at the beach, the moon appeared to be a reddish color when it first came up; a few hours later the moon was much higher in the sky and looked white."

- Have students make and record observations of the moon over a month and report their observations. "The moon appears to be different shapes at different times of the month."

- Show a time-lapse video clip and have students summarize what they observed. "As evening passes, the moon changes its position in the sky."

Phenomena and Student Performances

Observing phenomena prompts questions. Humans are naturally inquisitive and curious creatures. We use science to seek answers to questions and explain the natural world. Developing specific questions often leads to data and information that may prompt new questions and a revision of current thinking. Student experiences in science should include the ability to develop well-formulated questions that can be investigated.

Engaging with phenomena using science and engineering practices and crosscutting concepts. The goal of science is finding a single, coherent, and comprehensive explanation for a range of related phenomena (NRC, 2012). Seeing science as a suite of practices shows that gathering, reasoning, and communicating reasoning are components of a larger ensemble of performances. Crosscutting concepts provide consistent touchstones that support students' conceptual understanding of the phenomena under study in various disciplines.

Explaining the causes of phenomena using core ideas. Core ideas can be applied to explain and predict a variety of phenomena that occur in people's everyday lives. Students learn and demonstrate proficiency with core ideas by engaging in knowledge-building practices to explain and make informed decisions. Conceptual understanding builds when students connect new concepts to other related ideas and see these interconnections as they construct explanations.

Selecting and Using Grade-Appropriate Phenomena

In our work with thousands of teachers we have found that focusing science instruction on grade-appropriate phenomena is an important, but challenging shift for teachers. This approach to instruction requires students to explain the causes of phenomena using grade-appropriate core ideas and crosscutting concepts. Notice that students are explaining, rather than teachers. In this way, students are the investigators, increasing their understanding of science.

All children are naturally curious and capable of investigating phenomena in their world. Young children come to school with a variety of prior knowledge and skill upon which to build science learning experiences. They can generate and evaluate evidence to support explanations. Students can develop questions, plan and carry out investigations to gather data, and reflect on modifying explanations in light of new evidence.

Phenomena presented in grade-appropriate ways are most meaningful when related to students' experiences. Characteristics of useful phenomena include relevant every day or family experiences which require students to use core ideas, practices, and crosscutting concepts to make sense of phenomena. Progressions of core ideas can be found at the *Going3DwithGRC* website and in *NGSS* Appendices E, F, and G.

Students' ability to understand and explain phenomena develops over time. High school students generally have more sophisticated explanations of a phenomenon than elementary students. In the upper grades, students focus on constructing explanations for how and/or why phenomena occur; while in lower grades, student investigations often center on what happens or whether the evidence supports an explanation for the phenomena. The following example illustrates this difference between elementary and high school. The example focuses on differences in the sophistication of core ideas about energy transformations. The elementary school grades use the idea of a "black box" to present the idea that energy is transformed, which avoids delving into the details of how the transformation occurs. High school explanations focus on the mechanism for how energy transformations occur.

Figure 1.2 Example of Differences in Explanations and Models Across Grade Levels and the Use of "Black Boxes"

Lesson Performance Expectations for Explanations	
Elementary Explanation	High School Explanation
Performance: Construct an explanation for how the system of the hand crank flashlight changes energy of motion into light energy.	Performance: Construct an explanation for how the system of the hand crank flashlight changes energy of motion into light energy.
Energy of motion is transferred from my hand to move the handle on the flashlight. Moving the handle causes the gears to turn and spin the magnet inside the flashlight.	Energy of motion is transferred from the motion of the hand into the motion of the gears inside the flashlight. The motion of the gears causes a magnet to spin inside a coil of copper wire.
Black Box Explanation: <u>The energy is changed from the kinetic energy of motion to electrical energy.</u>	The moving magnet causes an electric current to move in the wire. When a magnetic field moves through a coil of copper wire, the electrons in the wire begin to move causing an electric current. Therefore, energy of motion is transformed into electrical energy.
The electrical energy that is produced moves through the wires towards the light bulb.	The electrical energy that is produced is transferred through other wires to the light bulb.
Black Box Explanation: <u>The electrical energy is changed into light energy in the light bulb.</u>	The electrical energy is transformed into light energy in the light bulb. The light bulb is an LED. The way electricity is changed into light in an LED is by the movement of electrons from one semiconductor to another semiconductor.
Note. In 4th grade, some attention should be focused on the concept of energy transfer and the idea that energy is transformed.	Note. A high school physics explanation may include the structure and function of an LED, however, this is beyond the scope of *NGSS*.

Lesson Performance Expectations for Model	
Performance: Develop a model to show *that* energy is both transferred and transformed in the system of the hand crank flashlight.	Performance: Develop a model to support an explanation of *how* energy is transferred and transformed in the system of the hand crank flashlight.

Elementary School and High School Models of the System Transfers and Transformations of Energy	
Elementary School Model	**High School Model**
 ME= Motion Energy EE = Electrical Energy LE = Light Energy ME-hand moves gear EE- motion changed to electricity by magnets ME LE- electricity is changed to light	INPUT Energy of motion is transferred from the moving hand to the mechanical energy of the lever that spins the wheels in the flashlight. TRANSFORM Energy of motion is converted into electrical energy when the magnet spins through a coil of copper wire, and cause electrons to move in the wire and produce an electric current. TRANSFER Electrical energy moves through the wire from the generator to the LED light. TRANSFORM Electrical energy is converted into light energy. Electrons are excited and move from one semiconductor to another and when the electrons return to a lower energy level, light is emitted. OUTPUT Light energy is transferred from the LED to the surroundings as light.

In this example, learning in the earlier grades consists of an explanation that energy is transformed without the details of the mechanism by which energy is transformed. In later grades, details include how a magnet moving through a coil can induce an electric current. For this phenomenon, it is acceptable for students in elementary school to have "black boxes" in which they identify the transformation but without describing the mechanism (how) of the change. In later grades, students begin to think about how energy is transformed within these black boxes. Students use crosscutting concepts and core ideas to develop explanations for the mechanisms causing the transformation of energy. Teachers should recognize learning as a progression that requires coherence along the instructional pathway.

The black box approach is useful when establishing developmentally appropriate explanations. A student's grade level, degree of conceptual understanding, and background experience are all factors in establishing a developmentally appropriate explanation. Student explanations expand beyond the black box as the degree of sophistication with core ideas and crosscutting concepts develop.

Using phenomena to engage students in science learning requires several decisions on the part of the teacher to ensure that the phenomena support productive learning. The list below takes several ideas about phenomena and puts them into a simplified set of attributes to consider when selecting phenomena for classroom use. There are other possible criteria (e.g., cost, safety, time) you may wish to add to your own list.

Attributes of phenomena for engaging students in science learning include
1. Observable to students, either directly or indirectly using available tools (e.g., microscopes, telescopes, electronic probes, videos, and/or reliable sources.)

2. Interesting to activate students' natural curiosity.

3. Relevant and build upon students' experiences beyond the classroom.

4. Sophisticated enough for students to continue thinking about it beyond a single class period.

5. Grade-level appropriate in terms of how students gather data and information.

6. Requires students to use core ideas and crosscutting concepts consistent with the grade-level to construct explanations for the causes of the phenomena.

A phenomenon can be used across many grade levels, and is not generally tied to a single grade level. However, the standards for a specific grade level establish that some phenomena are more useful than others. The way we present phenomena and the expectation for student performances are grade-level specific. Figure 1.3 provides an example of phenomena and the grade-level core ideas students use to understand the causes of these phenomena.

In Figure 1.3, an example of related phenomena is shown across grade-levels. The explanations from higher grade-level students will be more sophisticated but based on the same underlying strands of core ideas. The core ideas within these strands and student performances change as the explanations become more sophisticated across the grades. Chapter 3 explores this way of looking at an observation of a phenomenon across the grade-bands and the supporting performances to make sense of that phenomenon.

The teacher's role is to sequence instruction and organize student experiences in ways that support student learning. Making sense of phenomena engages students in investigations and provides a useful and authentic way for students to learn science. Learning science is more than merely knowing science content; it requires learning the reasoning structures that support students making sense of the world beyond the classroom (Moulding & Bybee, 2017).

Figure 1.3 Phenomenon Across Grade Levels

Interactions of an object with another object can be explained and predicted using the concept of forces, which can cause a change in motion of one or both of the interacting objects. An individual force acts on one particular object and is described by its strength and direction. The strengths of forces can be measured and their values compared (National Research Council, 2012, p. 114)

	Grade-Related Science Phenomena or Engineering Challenges	Example of Grade-Level Specific Lesson Performances Core Ideas from Strands PS2.A, PS2.B, PS1.A
Kindergarten	Kites fly best on windy days.	Construct an explanation for why the pushes and pulls on the kite causes it to fly better on a windy day. PS2.A: Pushes and pulls can have different strengths and directions. (K-PS2-1), (K-PS2-2)
Grade 5	A flat sheet of paper falls slower than a wadded up sheet of paper.	Develop and use a model to support an explanation for how the forces acting on the paper that causes the flat sheet to fall slower than the wadded-up piece of paper. PS1.A: Matter of any type can be subdivided into particles that are too small to see, but even then the matter still exists and can be detected by other means.(5-PS1-1) PS2.B: The gravitational force of Earth acting on an object near Earth's surface pulls that object toward the planet's center (5-PS2-1) PS2.A: Each force acts on one particular object and has both a strength and a direction. An object at rest typically has multiple forces acting on it, but they add to give zero net force on the object. Forces that do not sum to zero can cause changes in the object's speed or direction of motion. (3-PS2-1)

Figure 1.3 Phenomenon Across Grade Levels, continued		
Middle School	Develop a paper airplane that when dropped can glide a distance of 2X when dropped from a height of 1X.	Construct an explanation for how the designed structure of the glider changes the force acting on the glider to cause it to glide further. PS2.A: The motion of an object is determined by the sum of the forces acting on it; if the total force on the object is not zero, its motion will change. The greater the mass of the object, the greater the force needed to achieve the same change in motion. For any given object, a larger force causes a larger change in motion. (MS-PS2-2) PS1.A: Matter of any type can be subdivided into particles that are too small to see, but even then the matter still exists and can be detected by other means.(5-PS1-1) PS2.B: The gravitational force of Earth acting on an object near Earth's surface pulls that object toward the planet's center. (5-PS2-1)
High School	When a wave at the beach hits me it can knock me off my feet, but a gust of wind moving at the same speed does not cause me to move.	Construct an explanation supported by evidence for the causes of water transferring a greater momentum than the same volume of air. PS2.A: Momentum is defined for a particular frame of reference; it is the mass times the velocity of the object. (HS-PS2-2) In any system, total momentum is always conserved. PS1.A: In a liquid, the molecules are constantly in contact with others; in a gas, they are widely spaced except when they happen to collide. (MS-PS1-4) PS1.A: The amount (weight) of matter is conserved when it changes form, even in transitions in which it seems to vanish. (5-PS1-2)

The following list provides insights into how to describe and use phenomena for instruction. The way in which students encounter phenomena determines whether they will become curious and be motivated to investigate phenomena. These four statements about phenomena are followed by a list of "Phenomenon" and "Not Phenomenon." Both are considering the use of phenomena for teaching and learning science.

1. Phenomena are observations, events, and facts that can be investigated and explained using science.

2. Phenomena cause students to wonder and motivate them to ask questions.

3. Phenomena lead students to plan and carry out investigations.

4. Phenomena are NOT questions, explanations, concepts, theories, or activities.

Figure 1.4 Comparing Examples of Phenomenon and Non-examples of Phenomenon	
Phenomenon	Not Phenomenon
▪ When dry ice is placed in warm water, bubbles of fog rise into the air.	▪ What causes more bubbles of fog to come off dry ice placed in warm water than dry ice placed in cold water? (question)
▪ I saw mushrooms growing in a circle in my backyard.	▪ Mushrooms are a member of the fungi kingdom. (classification)
▪ A piece of steel wool weighs more after rusting than it did before rusting.	▪ Matter is conserved. (concept) ▪ The mass of steel wool increases when it rusts by the mass of oxygen from the air that reacted with the iron. (explanation)
▪ Some, but not all, squirrels can fly from tree to tree.	▪ Flying squirrels inherit characteristics from their parents. (explanation)
▪ My shadow changes position throughout the day.	▪ Using a tetherball pole, chalk, and a clock, track and record changes in the position of a shadow from the pole to use as evidence of the motion of the sun. (activity)

Analogous Phenomena

Analogous phenomena are multiple phenomena with the same causes. Science phenomena travel in packs, and this helps students build a repertoire of analogous phenomena that serve as examples to support conceptual models of the causes of phenomena. When students are making sense of a novel phenomenon, they can rely on the conceptual models and crosscutting concepts previously used to make sense of an analogous phenomenon. The conceptual models and crosscutting concepts students apply to their science learning have existed for decades. Students do not need to confirm or prove these conceptual models and concepts, rather students apply the three dimensions to make sense of novel phenomena in their own world.

Making sense of phenomena by applying existing knowledge helps students conceptualize the learning so it becomes part of their daily way of viewing the world (NASEM, 2019). The Core Ideas in the *Framework* are a set of very powerful science ideas, appropriate for students in grades K-12, that can help explain a wide range of everyday phenomena. Because there is an overwhelming number of phenomena and only a limited set of Core Ideas, there must be many phenomena that can be explained using these same ideas. Students apply science ideas and concepts learned in previous investigations to help make sense of similar phenomena in and beyond the classroom. We call these analogous phenomena.

Engaging students with analogous phenomena help them to develop a deeper understanding of core ideas and crosscutting concepts, which can be used to make sense of phenomena beyond the classroom. Ultimately, we want students to use ideas productively to understand many phenomena in the natural world (NRC, 2007). Analogous phenomena are a way to move students toward applying their science learning to understand phenomena in novel contexts, an important learning goal for science education.

Figure 1.5 *Examples of Phenomenon and Analogous Phenomenon*	
Phenomenon	**Analogous Phenomenon**
▪ An ice cube left on the countertop melts.	▪ A puddle of water observed on the playground in the morning was gone by afternoon. ▪ A mug of cocoa sitting on the table too long gets cold. ▪ Chocolate candy melts in your hand.
▪ The sun rises and sets each day.	▪ The moon rises about 50 minutes later each day. ▪ In the northern hemisphere, we see the constellation Orion in the winter months, but not in summer. ▪ When it is morning in Hawaii it is afternoon in New York.
▪ In Utah, grass grows faster in May than in July.	▪ The willow trees near the river are larger than the ones on the hillside. ▪ In spring, blades of grass seem to have more water inside of them than in summer. ▪ Cattle grow faster when they eat more hay.

Student Science Performances

Three-dimensional science performances are a powerful way for teachers to direct student learning. Engaging students in science performances is more than having them do hands-on activities. It means students engage in science and engineering practices, using core ideas and crosscutting concepts in three-dimensional science performances that lead to explanations for the causes of phenomena. Curiosity motivates learning; more importantly for science education, relevant phenomena lead to students asking more meaningful questions. Three-dimensional science performances within lessons provide a structure to guide student learning. Each performance directs students in a logical sequence from gathering data and information, to reasoning about explanations for the causes of the phenomenon, and to developing and using arguments for how the data, information, and core ideas and concepts are used as evidence to support an explanation for the causes of the phenomenon.

> *"Science investigation and engineering design should be the central approach for teaching and learning science and engineering" (NASEM, 2019, p. 275).*

The examples of performances shown in Figure 1.6 illustrate how the three dimensions can be written as descriptors of student engagement. The NGSS and other state standards are written in a similar fashion. These four performance expectations may be used to reflect on how student performance expectations change across grade-levels. Notice how the K-2 performance focuses on "that" and "what" statements, while the higher grade-levels address "how" and "why" statements. This is typical for lesson performance expectations as well as standards. This articulation represents the building of science ideas and concepts across the grade-levels. This idea will be further developed in Chapter 3.

Figure 1.6   Examples of Student Science Performances for the Same Core Idea Across Grade-bands

Students Lesson Performances for Core Idea LS1.A: Structure and Function

K-2: Students construct an explanation for ways some plant structures help protect them from being eaten by animals.

3-5: Students obtain information from readings to investigate how the structures of three different types of tree seeds function to meet the needs of the plant.

MS: Students develop an argument for how the evidence they have gathered supports the explanation that a cell functions as a system that contributes to the functioning of the plant.

HS: Students develop and use a model to illustrate how the hierarchical organization of interacting systems function to support the motion of a chicken foot.

Observation of phenomena is a basic tenet of scientific investigation, but not the only way to engage students in learning science. For example, students may read about science and engineering that others have done, listen to lectures, watch videos, or play a game on their computer. However, as stated in the conclusions of the consensus report *Science and Engineering for Grades 6-12*, "Investigation and design are more effective for supporting learning than traditional teaching methods. They engage students in doing science and engineering, increase their conceptual knowledge of science and engineering, and improve their reasoning and problem-solving skills" (NASEM, 2019, p. 268).

Using Investigations in Teaching and Learning Science

Students learn by doing. Engaging students in the Investigation of natural phenomena and engineering design increases their conceptual understanding of the natural and engineered world. Investigation (capital I) is the process of science, which when used as the center of instruction improves students' reasoning and problem-solving skills. Viewing Investigation as the overarching process of doing science helps teachers to better see the roles of each of the science and engineering practices within the broader endeavor of engaging in science.

Engaging students in Investigation requires multiple practices, especially the *Framework*'s practice number 3 - *plan and carry out an investigation* (lower case i). Students use a suite of practices when engaging in Investigation. Because plan and carry out an investigation is so important within Investigation, it deserves a closer examination.

Figure 1.7 lists various types of investigations. Experiments are just one type of investigation. Other types of investigation include observational studies, using data from others' investigations, designing and testing solutions to engineering challenges, and researching information from reliable sources.

Science Experiments. Some investigations require students to plan and carry out experiments in which they change one variable (independent variable), monitor and measure the effects on a second variable (dependent variable), and control the other variables/conditions. Science experiments provide students with a way to obtain evidence to support explanations for the causal relationship between two variables.

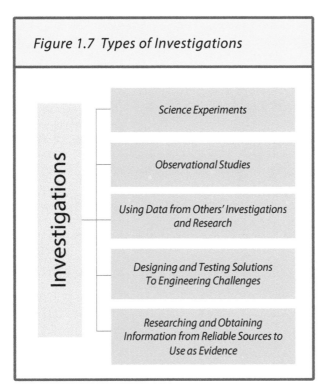

Figure 1.7 Types of Investigations

Investigations

- Science Experiments
- Observational Studies
- Using Data from Others' Investigations and Research
- Designing and Testing Solutions To Engineering Challenges
- Researching and Obtaining Information from Reliable Sources to Use as Evidence

Observational Studies. Some investigations are observational studies or field observations. In these investigations, planning involves deciding how to appropriately collect samples of data under various conditions despite not being in direct control of the environment, variables, and/or subjects being observed.

Using Data from Others' Investigations and Research. One of the ways students can engage in investigations when equipment or supplies are not available, is to use data sets from others. The use of large data sets from science agencies (e.g., NASA, NOAA, and USGS) is increasingly more available for students to analyze and use in investigations.

Designing and Testing Solutions to Engineering Challenges. Student investigations include the testing of solutions to engineering designs. Experiments to test engineering designs require students to determine relevant variables, ways to measure and collect data, and the most useful means to analyze data to provide evidence of effectiveness, efficiency, and/or durability of various designs, consistent with the criteria and constraints of the defined problem.

Researching and Obtaining Information from Reliable Sources to Use as Evidence. Often student investigations involve using information they have gathered from reliable sources. This approach requires students to document the sources and apply the information in reasoning about the causes of phenomena.

The vision for science education described in the *Framework* and *NGSS*, emphasizes engaging students in science performances. These performances include students applying their knowledge and skills to make sense of the world in which they live. This requires a major shift in science instruction, moving away from teaching "finished science" that describes the science we know and moving toward using science as a tool to make sense of phenomena. Investigations are the most effective way to create teachable moments for science learning.

Investigation provides opportunities for students to gather data and information needed to develop evidence. The science discourse that occurs as students gather data and information is important to science learning. This discourse may focus on developing questions to seek meaning from patterns, cause and effect relationships among variables, and the significance of inconsistent data. In-depth discussions about data and information help students to understand the nature of science as a social enterprise.

Investigation includes evaluating information and interpreting data to reason how the evidence supports explanations and arguments. Students often reason in group and/or class discussions. It is important for students to engage in civil discourse as they reason. Investigations create meaningful opportunities for each member of the classroom to argue their reasoning. The classroom discourse centers on ideas and logical reasoning and not on individuals. Investigation creates opportunities for developing a positive classroom learning culture.

Investigation provides opportunities for students to communicate the evidence they have developed. The presentation of this evidence occurs within the artifacts of learning created by students (e.g., writing, models, and oral presentations of explanations). Artifacts help students organize and share their thinking. These artifacts may reveal students' initial thinking but should progress over time to present more sophisticated reasoning as students revise their thinking in light of new evidence and others' ideas. Investigations create opportunities for teachers to engage students in learning about the nature of science and the role of evidence in science. As students engage in a series of coherent science performances, they come to

realize that scientific knowledge is based upon empirical evidence and gain insight into why scientific explanations are revised in light of new evidence.

The *Framework* and *NGSS* provide a clear vision for how science instruction can be structured to engage students in science performances. The *Framework* emphasizes that learning science includes knowing how to use the science and engineering practices. The *Framework* and subsequent National Academies reports including *Investigation and Design at the Center* provide insight into how the structure of instruction, specifically investigation is the best approach to engage students in science learning. The research presents a clear picture of instruction that is consistent with the GRC model for teaching and learning.

Summary - Science Phenomena and Student Science Performances

Science is the human endeavor of constructing causal explanations of phenomena. Teaching and learning science are active processes. The structure of instruction affects student learning and the likelihood of students transferring learning to make sense of phenomena beyond the classroom. The GRC instructional sequence engages students in three-dimensional science performances. The hallmark of the GRC is using a logical sequence of performances to engage students in using evidence to explain phenomena. GRC lessons always provide students with an opportunity to communicate their reasoning using writing, speaking, and/or models.

Curiosity motivates students to learn. Teachers can use students' curiosity to motivate learning by choosing phenomena that are interesting and engaging. Local and culturally relevant phenomena help support students' interest in science. Investigations engage students in doing science and increase conceptual knowledge of science reasoning (NASEM, 2019). The *NGSS* and state science standards that are consistent with the *Framework* present science performance expectations at the intersection of three dimensions. Working toward teaching and learning at the intersection of these three dimensions requires an understanding of each dimension as well as how they operate together.

Reflecting on Phenomena and Student Performances

Use the following prompts to initiate your reflections on Chapter 1.

1. Using Figure 1.1 as an example, describe five phenomena as observations that you might encounter in your daily life.

2. Why is presenting phenomena as an observation or event preferred to the presentation of phenomena as a teacher question or explanation?

3. How can you structure instruction to move students from observing a phenomenon to developing the evidence needed to support an explanation for the causes of the phenomenon?

4. Describe two phenomena that are analogous. How are these two phenomena analogous?

References

Moulding, B., & Bybee, R. (2017). *Teaching science is phenomenal: Using phenomena to engage students in three-dimensional science performances consistent with the NRC framework and the NGSS*. Washington, UT: ELM Tree Publishing.

National Academies of Sciences, Engineering, and Medicine. (2018). *How people learn II: Learners, contexts, and cultures*. Washington, DC: The National Academies Press.

National Academies of Sciences, Engineering, and Medicine. (2019). *Science and engineering for grades 6-12: Investigation and design at the center*. Washington, DC: The National Academies Press.

National Research Council. (2007). *Taking science to school: Learning and teaching science in grades k-8*. Washington, DC: The National Academies Press.

National Research Council. (2012). *A framework for k-12 science education: Practices, crosscutting concepts, and core ideas*. Washington, DC: The National Academies Press.

Notes

Chapter 2
Practices and Student Science Performances

STUDENTS learn science by doing science. The science and engineering practices define what students are doing in science. Inquiry is still part of science instruction: the practices do not replace inquiry as described in the National Science Education Standards (NRC, 1996), but define more clearly what successful student inquiry looks like. The practices are the doing component of three-dimensional science standards. When students engage in science investigations, they are engaged in the practices of science and engineering. They are making sense of phenomena as they ask questions, collect and analyze data, generate and utilize evidence, and develop models to support explanations and solutions.

> *Throughout this book, we use the term practices to mean the science and engineering practices as defined in the Framework.*

Engaging in the practices of science creates meaningful and memorable learning experiences for all students. These experiences pique students' curiosity and lead to greater interest and identity with science (NASEM, 2019). As described in the *Framework*, the science and engineering practices are not intended to be done in isolation, but rather used along with crosscutting concepts and core ideas to make sense of phenomena.

The *Framework* describes eight practices that scientists and engineers use as part of their work. These practices are used to structure instruction and assessments in ways that engage students in the practices similar to how they are used by scientists.

The Practices are What Students Do in Science

Science is something we do. Much like playing a sport or musical instrument — we engage students in science performances. The practices describe the doing for both scientists and students. In our science classrooms, students use the practices to make sense of phenomena. When students engage in practices, it promotes the development of critical 21st-century skills (Wagner, 2008), underlined here in relationship to the practices. Asking questions promotes curiosity. Obtaining and evaluating information, and analyzing data promotes students' abilities to access and analyze information. Planning investigations, developing models, and constructing explanations promote creativity. Communicating written and oral explanations and arguments promote effective oral and written communication. In general, engaging in practices promotes initiative, adaptability, agility, and collaboration among students.

Figure 2.1 Science and Engineering Practices

1. Asking questions (science and engineering) and defining problems (engineering)
   Students asking questions is a fundamental way to gather relevant data and information in the process of making sense of phenomena. Students develop questions that can be answered using empirical evidence. Often, initial questions are refined by individual reflection, small group discussion, and whole class discussion. We refer to this process as developing questions for a purpose. In engineering, the process of gathering information begins with defining a problem. Students ask questions to define an engineering problem, determine criteria for a successful solution, and identify constraints.

2. Developing and using models
   Students use models in several ways to gather information using charts, simulations, or physical models that generate data. Models can be used to reason, make predictions, and develop and communicate ideas with others. They may be used across the gather, reason, and communicate reasoning performances. Students refine models as their conceptual understanding develops.

3. Planning and carrying out investigations
   Students conduct investigations in the field, classroom, or anywhere they encounter phenomena. Investigations should foster the sense-making complexities of doing science including how to structure data. Students engage in investigations designed for making choices and deciding what to measure and record. This creates opportunities in the classroom for students to compare and share, which leads to refinements of the planned investigation based on what works and what does not. Engaging students in doing investigations about natural phenomena increases their understanding of how the world works.

4. Analyzing and interpreting data
   Students connect information gathered in investigations to explanations, models, or arguments through a transformation of data into evidence. Data refers to observations or measurements that are recorded for subsequent analysis. Data becomes evidence when it is used to support or refute an explanation. Students may use calculators, computers, models, graphical interpretation, and statistical analysis to make sense of data. These tools and techniques are used to seek patterns and significant features of the data where meaning can be recognized and extracted. The process of interpreting data involves assigning meaning to collected data and determining the significance and implications for using the data as evidence.

5. Using mathematics and computational thinking

Students use computational thinking when they integrate human thinking with the power of computational processes and technology to better understand the world. Computational thinking involves using human creativity and imagination to make computers useful to better understand our world and solve problems. Using mathematics and computational thinking involves a range of processes for reasoning to construct meaning by way of simulations, statistically analyzing data, and recognizing, expressing, and applying quantitative relationships.

6. Constructing explanations (science/engineering) and designing solutions to problems engineering)

Students construct explanations supported by evidence to provide an account of the most plausible mechanisms causing phenomena. Students should be able to construct coherent explanations of phenomena consistent with accepted science laws, models, theories, and/or explanations. Designing solutions to engineering problems require students to design a systematic process for considering the problem, determining constraints, and accommodating criteria. Solutions result from a process of balancing competing criteria of desired functions, technological feasibility, cost, safety, aesthetics, and compliance with legal requirements.

7. Engaging in argument from evidence

Students develop arguments for how the evidence supports an explanation. Each line of evidence is argued to determine if the evidence supports or refutes an explanation. Argumentation is the process of carefully ruling out alternative explanations and building the case that the data collected is sufficient and appropriate to serve as evidence for the current explanation. Arguments in science do not require disagreement and are often for the purpose of gaining confidence in an explanation. Students engage in argumentation to clarify models, the interpretation of data, and experimental designs. Engineering uses reasoned arguments to determine the best solution to solve a problem. The goal/purpose of engineering is to design the best possible solution to a problem related to a human want or need.

8. Obtaining, evaluating, and communicating information

The process of obtaining, evaluating, and communicating information is used by students to gather information, determine the validity of the sources, and put the information into contexts that others can understand the meaning of the information. In the 21st century, students have devices they can use to gather information quickly and efficiently, but the information must be carefully evaluated before it can be used. Writing, models, and speaking are critical ways for students to communicate their thinking. Science requires the ability to derive meaning from texts, including the internet and lectures, to evaluate the validity of the information acquired, and to integrate that information. Science advances when scientists can clearly and persuasively communicate their findings or learn about the findings of others.

Engaging students in practices should be purposeful in ways that simultaneously engage students in using the crosscutting concepts and core ideas to making sense of phenomena. This can be done by developing three-dimensional science **performances** that describe how and why students are engaging in doing science. These student performances combine practices and crosscutting concepts and require the use of core ideas. Lesson performances are structured with the three-dimensions in a way similar to the

NGSS performance expectations but are specific to the phenomenon under investigation. The following is an example of student performances from a lesson.

Practices and the GRC Sequence

Lesson Performance —Observe the picture of trees in snow and develop questions to investigate the causes of patterns you observe.

Figure 2.2 Tree Wells in Snow

Just like scientists, students engage in a suite of practices to make sense of phenomena often extending over multiple class periods. It is helpful to think of this sequence in terms of three distinct components, each with its own specific purpose: Gather, Reason, and Communicate Reasoning (Moulding, Bybee, & Paulson, 2015). Making sense of phenomena requires that students first **gather** information and data, and use this information and data as evidence to **reason** causal relationships. Finally, students **communicate** their reasoning through writing, speaking, and/or models. The Gather, Reason, and Communicate Reasoning (GRC) instructional sequence and the role of practices in this sequence are described in Figure 2-3.

Gather— When students encounter a phenomenon, they first need an opportunity to develop questions to guide the sense-making of the phenomenon. Some of these questions are testable and lead to planning and carrying out investigations that provide data. Other questions lead to obtaining additional information. As students continue to make sense of the phenomenon, additional questions arise. Not all student-generated questions can or should be investigated, but further discussion of student questions leads to developing questions to be investigated. During the investigation, additional questions surface that guide student thinking about the phenomenon. The questions "How did that happen?" or "Why did that happen?" should move toward "What mechanisms caused this to happen?" and "What conditions were necessary for this to happen?" (NRC, 2012).

> *The **gather** component of a lesson provides students with data and information they will analyze and evaluate to develop the evidence needed for reasoning the causes of phenomena.*

Planning and carrying out investigations can take the form of experiments, in which a variable is changed (independent variable) that causes a change in another variable (dependent variable), while keeping other variables constant. However, experiments are not always the best way to investigate all phenomena. In some areas of life, earth, and space sciences, experiments are not reasonable or useful. In those cases, investigations may take the form of observational studies, finding data and other information from books or other resources and online. Various types of investigations were described in Chapter 1, Figure 1.7. In all cases, the purpose of an investigation is to determine the causes of phenomena. Gathering includes developing and using models to collect data and using models to generate data when it is impractical to study the phenomena directly. For example, students can use charts to organize data from experiments, use stream tables as a physical model to collect data on weathering and erosion, use computer simulations to investigate the effects of gravity on the projectile motion on other planets, or use simulations to study interactions in ecosystems. Computational thinking helps students to integrate the power of human thinking with the capabilities of computational processes and technologies for gathering data and information.

Figure 2.3 Science and Engineering Practices Organized within a GRC Sequence

The practices are not specific to a part of the sequence and may be used at any time. In this figure, the practices are color-coded to identify linkages. Red = obtaining, evaluating, and communicating information; Blue = constructing explanations and engaging in argument from evidence; Orange = analyzing and interpreting data and using mathematical/ computational thinking; Aqua = developing and using models.

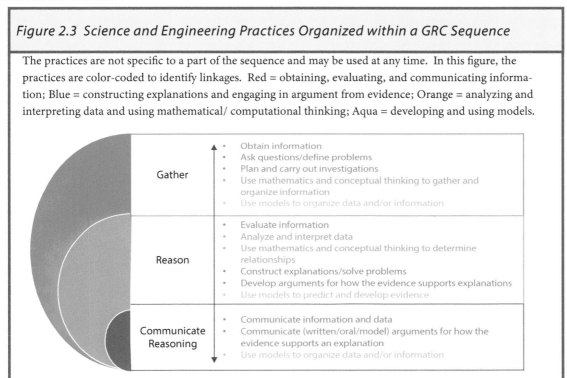

Adapted from Moulding, Bybee, & Paulson, 2015

Reason— Students use the data and information they gathered to make sense of phenomena. Data from investigations do not have meaning unless analyzed and presented in ways that reveal useful patterns and relationships. Analyzing data is the process by which data is organized using a combination of charts, tables, graphs, groupings of similar items, and statistical analysis. Mathematics is a tool students can use to analyze data and find meaningful patterns. Through statistical analysis students determine if the data are significant or meaningful in the context in which it is being used. In the end, analysis of data provides us with a judgment as to whether the data is useful as evidence or just coincidental. Students evaluate the information they collected to ensure it is relevant to the phenomenon being investigated. Computational thinking can be used to interpret data, identify patterns, and determine relationships by using computer simulations, mathematical representations, visualizations, or computer analysis to develop evidence.

> The **reasoning** component of lessons is critical because it teaches students to move beyond simple communication of collected data and information toward constructing explanations for the causes of phenomena. Structuring lessons with GRC engages students in reasoning with a purpose and a purpose for reasoning.

Students interpret data to determine how it can be used as evidence to support or refute models and explanations. Students use their interpretation of data and information to develop and use models as they make sense of the phenomenon. Models are used in the reasoning component to determine the interactions among parts of the system. Students use models to visualize the important components of systems and the interactions of matter with forces, energy, and among organisms. Models help students to track how energy flows into, through and/or out of systems, and how this affects the matter in the system and its interactions. Models can be physical models, drawn models, equations, or computer models. In combination with the data and information collected, models are used as sense-making tools to construct explanations for the causes of phenomena. Students use the evidence they gathered to develop arguments for how the evidence supports an explanation. Mathematical reasoning is used to determine the relevance and significance of the data as part of the argument. "Science instruction should be designed to engage students in reasoning with a purpose and a purpose for reasoning" (Duschl, 2017).

Communicate Reasoning— Once students have constructed explanations and developed arguments, it is meaningful for them to communicate their reasoning. Students communicate reasoning to better understand the relationship of the evidence to their explanation. Preparing and sharing this reasoning with the teacher and other students is essential to science learning. Students use writing, speaking, and models to communicate explanations, and to make then argue for how their evidence supports an explanation. Students may communicate other information (e.g., how they planned and carried out their investigation, discussions about resolving differences in ideas among the group, how they solved problems encountered while making measurements). Students provide and receive critiques about their explanations and arguments by citing relevant evidence and reasoning.

The communicate reasoning component in the GRC process is essential for creating a formal opportunity for students to make their thinking visible to themselves and others for the purpose of reflecting on and evaluating their reasoning. This process is similar to scientists communicating their scientific findings to the science community for peer review. Scientists engage in this process to determine the strongest possible explanation the evidence can support. In science education, students seek the best possible way to make their thinking visible to themselves and others for the purpose of evaluating their reasoning. The communicate reasoning component creates an opportunity for students to align their reasoning with accepted science concepts, principles, and theories. There are several instructional strategies (e.g., poster sessions, oral reports, written papers) teachers use in this component of the GRC process. The communicate reasoning component nurtures the development of individual reflection and brings students together in a community of informed learners.

Another benefit of engaging students in the practices is the opportunity for meaningful ongoing formative assessment. The practices are an essential dimension for both instruction and assessment. When students develop questions, plan investigations, and use data and information, teachers gain insights into student reasoning. The models, explanations, and arguments provide valuable information about students' conceptual models and the degree to which they accurately apply core ideas and crosscutting concepts in their reasoning. *NGSS* and state standards aligned to the *Framework* use the practices to direct the performance expectations (standards). A coherent sequence of practices is an effective way to direct student performances within a lesson and/or instructional unit.

> The **communicate reasoning** component of the instructional sequence focuses on students presenting their reasoning for the causes of phenomena and reflecting on their own and others learning. This component of the GRC provides meaningful artifacts to use in formative and summative assessments.

The selection of a specific *NGSS* performance expectations should inform, but not limit classroom instruction and assessment. The *NGSS* performance expectations provide a "snapshot" of students' abilities to make sense of phenomena, which is appropriate for summative assessment but too limiting for classroom instruction. Examples of *NGSS* performance expectations for each of the practices are shown in Figure 2.4.

Although the performance expectations in standards should not limit teaching and learning, they do have implications for instruction. The NGSS performance expectations clearly establish the criteria for evidence of student proficiency in science. This criterion is described as three-dimensional science performances using the practices, core ideas, and crosscutting concepts; hence classroom instruction should be based on similar three-dimensional performances. The performances in classroom instruction should 1) engage students in myriad combinations of the three-dimensions, 2) assess more than the "snapshots" described in the standards, and 3) progress across a logical sequence of performances that move from being curious about a phenomenon to constructing explanations for the causes of analogous phenomena beyond the classroom. Science instruction should have an intentional sequence of performances that help students become proficient at using each of the practices with multiple crosscutting concepts and core ideas.

> ## Figure 2.4 Examples of NGSS Performance Expectations for Each of the Practices
>
> - **Ask questions** to determine cause and effect relationships of electric or magnetic interactions between two objects not in contact with each other. (Grade 3)
>
> - **Develop a model** to describe the movement of matter among plants, animals, decomposers, and the environment. (Grade 5)
>
> - **Plan and carry out an investigation** to provide evidence that feedback mechanisms maintain homeostasis. (Grades 9-12)
>
> - **Construct and interpret graphical displays of data** to describe the relationships of kinetic energy to the mass of an object and to the speed of an object. (Grades 6-8)
>
> - **Use mathematical representations** to describe a simple model for waves that include how amplitude is related to the energy in a wave. (Grades 6-8)
>
> - **Use evidence to construct an explanation** relating the speed of an object to the energy of that object. (Grade 4)
>
> - **Construct an argument supported by evidence** for how plants and animals (including humans) can change the environment to meet their needs. (Grade K)
>
> - **Communicate scientific information** that common ancestry and biological evolution are supported by multiple lines of empirical evidence. (Grades 9-12)

GRC lessons use a series of three-dimensional performances to describe what students do to investigate phenomena by gathering, reasoning, and communicating. Any of the lesson performances in the sequence may be used for formative assessment. Lesson performances are embedded assessments that become an integral part of the learning experience and measure students' development of three-dimensional learning over time (NASEM, 2019). The lesson performances make students' thinking visible. This creates opportunities for students and teachers to monitor the progress of learning across multiple performances and make appropriate adjustments to teaching and learning. Teachers can determine places within the sequence for class-level assessment of student progress by using pre-planned class discussions. Individual student performances with-

in the lesson can be used as a formal formative assessment **for** student learning, or as a summative assessment **of** student learning. Summative assessment may also be a separate performance task that engages students in making sense of phenomena that are analogous to the phenomena used in the lesson(s). Figure 2.5 is an example of a GRC sequence of three-dimensional lesson performances.

Several practices are used in the Snow Tree Wells lesson. Each practice is part of a sequence that directs student performances. The sequence of practices begins by developing questions and concludes with students communicating an argument for how the evidence supports their explanation. The Gathering practices in the investigation start with students exploring the phenomenon, which is a type of preliminary investigation (e.g., explore, observe, probe). Each of the performances has a purpose for advancing students' investigation of the phenomenon.

Figure 2.5 Example of a GRC Sequence of Lesson Performances

NGSS Performance Expectation: MS-PS4-2. Develop and use a model to describe that waves are reflected, absorbed, or transmitted through various materials.

Phenomenon: Several days after a snowfall, holes in the snow appear around tree trunks.

Group Performances

Gather
1. Observe the pictures of trees in snow and develop questions to investigate the causes of the patterns you observe.

Group Discussion about Good Questions to Plan an Investigation
2. Plan and carry out an investigation to obtain evidence for the causes of snow melting faster in one place than another.

3. Obtain information about how energy is changed from light energy to heat energy.

Reason
4. Develop a model of the relevant natural system to explain how light energy affects trees and snow differently.

5. Construct an explanation for the causes of holes appearing in the snow around the bases of trees.

Class Discussion
6. Revise and communicate a written explanation supported by evidence for how the interaction between radiation and matter causes holes in the snow around the base of trees.

Individual Performance

Communicate Reasoning
7. Develop an argument for how the evidence you gathered support your explanation for the causes of holes in the snow forming around the base of trees.

(Teaching Suggestions: The focus of the lesson is on transfer and transformation of energy. Light energy is transformed into heat energy that causes snow to melt. More snow melts where more light is absorbed and changed into heat. Performance #2 can be an experiment, a research investigation, or both. The lesson should focus on student understanding of the transformation of light energy into heat energy. The investigation assumes students know that ice melts when heated.)

Performance #1 - This leads to students developing questions to plan an investigation. Students ask questions to refine preliminary inquiries and observations about the phenomenon. Asking questions should move into developing questions as a process for students to brainstorm potential avenues for obtaining information or planning an investigation. This process is most effective when pairs of students work together to develop questions and then present and discuss their questions with their peers. This leads into a full class discussion about what constitutes "good questions."

Group Discussion About Good Questions The Snow Tree Wells lesson sequence uses a class discussion to refine and develop questions to guide the investigation. Teachers often place a discussion about the questions in the gathering portion of the lesson for students to refine the focus of the investigation. Discussion about any of the practices during the GRC sequence helps students develop an understanding of both the skill and knowledge specific to each practice. The *Framework* asserts engaging in scientific investigation requires not only skill but also the knowledge that is specific to each practice.

Performance #2 The Gather component of GRC lessons is used by students to gather data and information needed to develop evidence to support reasoning. The practice in the second performance engages students in planning and carrying out an investigation to gather data. This investigation can be an experiment, research, or both.

Performance #3 Following the experiment, students will obtain information by reading about how light energy is changed into heat energy. This may be a short reading but is necessary to support students' understanding of the transformation of energy to cause the phenomenon. Students will likely cite this reading as evidence to support their explanation for the cause of the phenomenon.

Performance #4 The Reasoning practices used in the investigation begin with students developing a model of the system in which the phenomenon occurs. Models of systems provide a structure for students to make sense of the system in terms of matter and energy. The inputs of energy in this system cause changes to the matter (snow). The relationship between the energy entering a system and the changes of matter within systems are useful performances for students to understand phenomena.

Performance #5 The next step in the sequence is for students to develop an explanation for the causes of the phenomenon. Students' explanations are based on data (observations and/or measurements) from

their investigations. Data can also be obtained from readings and used as evidence in support of explanations. When students write an explanation prior to the class discussion, they are more likely to productively participate in the discussion.

The **class discussion** provides teachers with an opportunity to highlight specific practices, core ideas, and crosscutting concepts within the context of the lesson. The discussion enables students to bring their ideas to the forefront and the teacher to guide the discussion toward a scientifically accurate explanation. This synthesis of ideas is enhanced by the teacher adding accurate language, ideas, and concepts in ways that move the discussion to a class-wide common understanding of a scientific explanation for the phenomenon. The teacher does this without telling students the explanation, but by bringing together the evidence and accurate information from students to develop a coherent classwide understanding of the science. Teachers can effectively orchestrate class discussions by using information gleaned from student group discussions, student writing from individual performances, and from student models.

The evidence students use to support their explanations as well as nuances, insights, and conceptualization of core ideas and crosscutting concepts is often the focus of the class discussion. The class discussion should lead to students transferring the learning to other phenomena from personal experiences of past investigations. Often the teacher elicits or offers examples of analogous phenomena in the discussion. When the teacher offers examples, it should be for the purpose of extending student thinking and eliciting examples.

Performances #6 & #7 Following the class discussion, students revise their explanations prior to working individually to develop an argument for how the evidence they have gathered support their explanation for the causes of the phenomenon. The evidence from the investigation may include descriptions of patterns of melting seen in multiple pictures, (e.g., no snow wells around trees immediately following new snowfalls, but wells appearing after a few sunny days.) Evidence may include 1) knowledge of how sunlight is changed to heat when it is absorbed by an object, 2) dark-colored objects absorb more light than white objects, (3) appearance of snow wells around nearby rocks and, 4) other lines of evidence. The students may use evidence from experiments with sticks or disks of various colors placed into the snow and left in the sunlight. While this investigation may not be practical in some climates, teachers in warmer climates can use analogous phenomena to investigate how light changes to heat.

The practice used in the Communicate Reasoning component of the lesson sequence is arguing from evidence. There is considerable reasoning involved in developing the argument; however, each component of the GRC lesson requires students to reason. When students are planning an investigation to gather data, they are reasoning about how to design the investigation to obtain meaningful results. When students are obtaining information, they are deciding on the best search terms or questions to use for finding relevant information. All lesson performances in the GRC require students to think—that is unless the teacher tells the student the explanation prior to the investigation.

In this lesson sequence, the "Individual Performance" is developing and presenting the argument for how the evidence students gathered supports the explanation for the causes of the phenomenon. The teacher decides at which point in the lesson students move from working in a group to working individually. Here, teachers could decide to have students revise their explanations individually or in groups before asking students to develop an argument individually. The teacher may decide to have students stay in groups through the argument. As always, these decisions are made by the professional teacher who knows the best approaches for their students at that particular time in the learning sequence.

This lesson provides students with knowledge, skills, and dispositions for doing science. The next step is for students to apply science learning to make sense of analogous phenomena beyond the classroom. There are thousands of phenomena that are analogous to the snow tree wells phenomenon. A few examples include

- The ice in a red solo cup melts faster than the ice in a white cup.

- My blue beach towel gets warmer than my brothers' white towel.

- On a hot summer day, I can walk barefoot on the concrete but not on the blacktop.

It is important for teachers to develop a clear expectation for students to find analogous phenomena beyond the classroom. This may be as simple as regularly asking students to share phenomena they see in their daily lives and then valuing their observation by letting them describe their own explanation. We should resist the temptation to tell students the answer and make clear our value for their wondering about the world.

Using GRC lessons to effectively teach science requires teachers to know (1) when to have students make decisions about investigations and when to provide direction, (2) what ideas and concepts students can discover and what ideas and concepts to provide, and (3) how to motivate students to learn and when to step back and let students be self-actualizing. These decisions greatly affect the learning of science and the degree to which students act on their curiosity and interest. This is an essential element of the art of teaching and, to be done well, requires a professional teacher.

Evidence and the Science and Engineering Practices

Science is a way of knowing that is based on evidence. In the *NGSS*, two practices specifically call out the use of evidence within the practice statements— *constructing explanations supported by evidence* and *arguing from evidence*. However, every practice is in the service of gathering, refining, or using evidence. Empirical evidence is the basis of knowing in science; as illustrated below, each of the practices engages students in gathering, analyzing, refining, evaluating, using or communicating the evidence that supports explanations.

1. Asking questions is a critical tool in the evidence-gathering process. Questions can be used to seek information, define problems, or design an investigation that gathers data to use as evidence.

2. Developing and using models is the process of determining relationships among variables to use as evidence, or using models to communicate how the evidence supports an explanation.

3. Planning and carrying out investigations is the process of gathering and organizing data that can be analyzed and interpreted to use as evidence.

4. Analyzing and interpreting data organizes gathered data to identify patterns and assign meaning that can be used as evidence.

5. Using mathematics and computational thinking provides the tools and techniques to gather data, find patterns and relationships in data and determine if the data is significant enough to use as evidence.

6. Constructing explanations requires students to generate explanations for the causes of phenomena supported by evidence.

7. Engaging in argument is rooted in the gathered evidence; students develop arguments for how the evidence supports or refutes an explanation.

8. Obtaining, evaluating, and communicating information is a series of practices that moves from gathering information to evaluating that information for validity and relevance, and finally communicating the information as evidence that supports an explanation.

Science is an endeavor in which we seek *evidence* to support explanations for the causes of phenomena. In this context, it makes sense that the practices — the doing of science — describe engaging students in the gathering of *evidence*, reasoning about the meaning of the *evidence*, reasoning about the relationship of the *evidence* to explanations, and communicating (arguing for) how the *evidence* supports explanations.

The nature of science is based on evidence. Science investigations seek evidence and science explanations require evidence. Science instruction should help students understand how the practices are related to gathering and using evidence. Classroom discussions about evidence and the nature of science should be a regular part of instruction. The use of evidence across the instructional sequence in GRC lessons should be made explicit to the student.

There are several underlying principles that are helpful to understanding how to use argumentation for science instruction. First, it is important to understand that arguments do not require disagreement. Rather, argumentation requires that students be unsure of their preliminary explanation and work toward gaining confidence in that explanation by either reconciling it with alternatives or bolstering the evidence in support of it. Student explanations can be presented as an equation, a model or part of a model, or other representation. Second, students can and should engage in scientific argumentation around issues that have a "right answer." Argumentation helps students develop a deeper understanding of the evidence that supports an explanation (Berland & Reiser, 2008). When students take time to consider alternative explanations, they deepen their understanding of the explanations they have evidence to support and their understanding of why other explanations are not supported by the available evidence.

Summary of Chapter 2 – Practices and Student Science Performances

The science and engineering practices are the doing component of science. Instruction that engages students in doing science should be organized around the practices. The GRC sequence leverages the practices as students use three-dimensional lesson performances to learn science. The GRC is both a strategy for student learning and an instructional sequence for designing lessons. The sequence of practices in a GRC lesson should prompt students to *be curious* about a phenomenon, *gather data* through investigations and information from texts, *analyze and interpret data* and *evaluate information*, *construct explanations* for the causes of the phenomenon, *develop arguments* for how the evidence they gathered supports or refutes their explanation, and then *communicate explanations* and *arguments* through writing, speaking, and using models. Across the GRC sequence, students use models to gather and organize data, to explain and predict phenomena, reason the relationships among variables, and communicate explanations to themselves and others (Moulding & Bybee, 2017).

Along the way, students develop a meaningful understanding of the crosscutting concepts and core ideas and how to apply them to make sense of phenomena. They develop a cadre of analogous phenomena that provide examples for applying concepts and ideas to make sense of phenomena. Students develop the skills and knowledge of the practices to use in investigating phenomena encountered beyond the classroom.

Teaching is a profession that requires considerable work on the part of a professional teacher to effectively engage students in science learning that is memorable and applicable beyond the classroom. The practices are essential for students to become proficient at engaging in science performances that yield science knowledge and skills that can be applied beyond the classroom. The GRC is a structure for teachers to effectively engage students in meaningful science performances.

In this chapter, we provided an example of student performances from one lesson entitled "Tree Snow Wells," which can be accessed along with other GRC lessons at the *Going3DwithGRC* website. This website has approximately 300 vetted GRC lessons across grades K-12. The lessons were developed by classroom teachers in 10 states.

Reflecting on Practices and Student Science Performances

Use the following prompts to initiate your reflections on Chapter 2.

1. Why is a suite of practices more effective for teaching and learning science than a single practice?

2. How are using practices to engage students in science performances different from traditional models of instruction?

3. Select and think about one practice your students use proficiently. Select and discuss a second practice your students struggle with; why do students struggle with some of the practices when they are proficient with others?

4. How are the NGSS performance expectations similar to and different from "Lesson Performances"?

5. Why are the practices central to using the GRC structure to guide teaching and learning?

References

Berland, L.K., & Reiser, B. (2008). Making sense of argumentation and explanation. *Science Education*, 93(1), 26-55.

Duschl, R.A. (2017, July). *Investigations & nature of science: Beyond planning and carrying out investigations. Presentation for committee on science investigations and engineering design experiences in grades 6-12.* Washington, DC: National Academies of Sciences, Engineering, and Medicine.

Moulding, B., Bybee, R., & Paulson, N. (2015). *A vision and plan for science teaching and learning: An educator's guide to a framework for k-12 science education, next generation science standards and state standards.* Salt Lake City, UT: Essential Teaching and Learning.

Moulding, B., & Bybee, R. (2017). *Teaching science is phenomenal: Using phenomena to engage students in three-dimensional science performances consistent with the NRC framework and the NGSS.* Washington, UT: ELM Tree Publishing.

National Academies of Sciences, Engineering, and Medicine. (2019). *Science and engineering for grades 6-12: Investigation and design at the center.* Washington, DC: The National Academies Press.

National Research Council. (1996). *National science education standards, national committee for science education standards and assessment.* Washington, DC: The National Academy Press.

National Research Council. (2012). *A framework for k-12 science education: Practices, crosscutting concepts, and core ideas.* Washington, DC: The National Academies Press.

Wagner, T. (2008). *The global achievement gap: Why even our best schools don't teach the new survival skills our children need-and what we can do about it.* New York, New York: Perseus Book Group.

Notes

Chapter 3

Using Crosscutting Concepts and Disciplinary Core Ideas

STUDENTS use crosscutting concepts and disciplinary core ideas to make sense of the natural and human-designed world and to support explanations for the causes of phenomena. The role of these two dimensions in teaching science has shifted. In the past, students' knowledge of these two dimensions was tested as the outcome of instruction; now students use crosscutting concepts and disciplinary core ideas in the process of making sense of phenomena. For students to use these two dimensions with fluency, core ideas and crosscutting concepts must become operationalized as conceptual understanding. There are important nuances that distinguish these two dimensions; however, they serve similar roles for students. Thus, crosscutting concepts and core ideas are addressed in this chapter first separately and then together.

Crosscutting Concepts

Crosscutting concepts can be used by students to make sense of phenomena across all science disciplines. The *Framework* describes seven science-specific crosscutting concepts that connect, focus, and organize science knowledge. The crosscutting concepts support students in developing a coherent and scientifically-informed view of the world. Students use the set of seven crosscutting concepts to 1) establish underlying causality, which is essential for making sense of phenomena; 2) develop an understanding of the system(s) being investigated; and 3) recognize and use patterns as evidence to support explanations and arguments. Crosscutting concepts are used as science-specific tools to make sense of natural phenomena and unify the study of science through common application across fields (NRC, 2012).

For years, students were expected to build knowledge of the crosscutting concepts without explicit instruction. In the new vision for science education, crosscutting concepts are common and familiar *touchstones* across all science disciplines, grade-levels, and for some concepts applied in other school subjects (e.g., cause and effect, systems, patterns). Explicit use of the crosscutting concepts, as well as their emergence in multiple disciplinary contexts, supports students' development of a cumulative, coherent, and versatile understanding of science and engineering. The crosscutting concepts provide students with coherence across science disciplines and a thread to begin unraveling the causes of phenomena in the world beyond the classroom. Emphasis is on coherence and sense-making rather than recitations, procedures, memorization of laws, and the use of scientific language. The *Framework* identifies seven crosscutting concepts, shown in Figure 3.1 with the word "system" highlighted in red for emphasis not found in the original *Framework* document.

Figure 3.1 *Crosscutting Concepts from* A Framework for K-12 Science Education

1. Patterns – Observed patterns of forms and events guide organization and classification. Patterns prompt questions about the factors that influence cause and effect relationships. Patterns are useful as evidence to support explanations and arguments.

2. Cause and Effect: Mechanism and explanation – Events have causes, sometimes simple, sometimes multifaceted and complex. A major activity of science is investigating and explaining causal relationships and the mechanisms by which they are mediated. Such mechanisms can then be tested across given contexts and used to predict and explain events in new contexts.

3. Scale, Proportion, and Quantity – In considering phenomena, it is critical to recognize what is relevant in different measures of size, time, and energy and to recognize how changes in scale, proportion, or quantity affect a system's structure or performance.

4. Systems and System Models – Defining the system under study—specifying its boundaries and making explicit a model of that system—provides tools for understanding and testing ideas that are applicable throughout science and engineering.

5. Energy and Matter: Flows, cycles, and conservation of energy and matter – Tracking fluxes of energy and matter into, out of, and within systems helps one understand the system's capabilities and limitations.

6. Structure and Function – An object's structure and shape determine many of its properties and functions. The structures, shapes, and substructures of living organisms determine how the organism functions to meet its needs within an environment.

7. Stability and Change – For natural and built systems alike, conditions of stability and rates of change provide the focus for understanding how the system operates and the causes of changes in systems.

The crosscutting concepts apply across all science disciplines and articulate across grade-levels. Teachers can make them explicit by including them within the structure of lessons and instruction. The crosscutting concepts help frame investigations, explanations, and arguments by focusing students on specific aspects of phenomena. For them to become an integral part of student thinking, it is important for teachers and students to use the crosscutting concepts consistently and accurately within class discussions. When they become familiar touchstones, students will use the crosscutting concepts as a lens to make sense of phenomena beyond the classroom.

Organizing the crosscutting concepts helps students and teachers use them more effectively. Figure 3.2 provides a way to organize the crosscutting concepts by how students use them to make sense of phenomena. Notice that several of the crosscutting concepts focus students on important aspects of systems, and that two crosscutting concepts describe causality.

Figure 3.2 Crosscutting Concepts Organized by Function for Making Sense of Phenomena		
Causality	Systems	Pattern
Cause and Effect Structure and Function	Systems are a useful way to describe phenomena in terms of the changes in matter, energy, and forces affecting the interaction among components of systems.	Patterns can be used as evidence to support explanations. They give observations greater meaning. Science seeks causes of naturally occurring patterns.
The things we study in science can be described in terms of cause and effect or how the structure determines the function.	Energy and Matter Stability and Change Scale, Proportion, Quantity	
	The proportion of components in a system affects how the system operates. Systems may operate differently at different scales and are affected by the quantity of components in the system.	Patterns

Often, the crosscutting concepts help students focus on specific aspects of the systems in which a phenomenon occurs (e.g., how the flow of energy into a system causes changes, how the proportion of components in a system change over time). Students make sense of phenomena by determining the system in which the phenomenon operates and how the system interacts with other systems to cause changes. **Systems** can be described in terms of (1) movement of matter and energy into, out of, or within systems; (2) scale of systems, and the quantity and proportion of components in systems; and (3) stability and/or changes occurring in systems.

In the following examples, the response is not meant to be revealed or provided to the students; instead students apply the crosscutting concepts and core ideas in pursuit of these explanations for the phenomena.

Examples of Systems

Energy and Matter

1. Phenomenon: Canada Geese can be observed flying north each Spring.

    Prompt: How do seasonal energy changes in the northern hemisphere affect the migration of geese?

    Response: Northern migration of Canada Geese follows the growth of grass. The grass growth increases as the quantity of sunlight increases in the Spring and puts more energy into northern ecosystems. Putting more energy into the system causes grass to grow faster.

2. Phenomenon: The wind speed of hurricane Maria slowed as it moved north.

    Prompt: How does changing the input of energy into a hurricane system affect wind speeds?

    Response: The wind speed of a hurricane increases as it passes over warmer ocean waters. Warmer water adds more energy to the hurricane system which increases wind speed. When the warm and humid air in the hurricane subsequently passes over colder water, it transfers energy back to the ocean and the wind speed in the hurricane system decreases.

3. Phenomenon: The recent eruption of the Kilauea volcano increased the size of Hawai'i.

    Prompt: How does the cycling of matter change the surface of Earth?

    Response: Molten rock material moves from the mantle to the crust and flows into the oceans to build more land.

Scale, Proportion, and Quantity

4. Phenomenon: Arches National Park has over 2000 natural stone arches that were formed over tens of thousands of years.

    Prompt: How do changes at the atomic scale cause large arches to form in Arches National Park?

    Response: Stone arches that can be over 300 feet high were formed by changes at the scale of atoms as the water caused the calcite holding the Entrada sandstone together to dissolve, leaving individual grains of sand.

5. Phenomenon: Nails near the Great Salt Lake rust faster than nails near Lake Erie.

    Prompt: How does the proportion of salt in water affect the rate of rusting?

    Response: The quantity of salt in water affects the proportion of ions in the water. This affects the rate electrons move from one atom to another which increases the rate that iron reacts with oxygen to form iron (III) oxide (rust).

6. Phenomenon: Carrot sticks are crisper when placed in freshwater than in saltwater.

    Prompt: How does the proportion of salt in water affect the crispness of vegetables?

    Response: The proportion of salt in water affects the proportion of ions in water. When the proportion of ions inside the cell is greater than the proportion of ions outside the cell, water moves from the system surrounding the carrot cells into the carrot cell system causing the cell to swell and the carrot stick to be crisper.

7. Phenomenon: The sand in the Imperial Valley of California has the same composition as the sand in the Grand Canyon.

    Prompt: What is the relationship between the quantity of sand weathered from the Grand Canyon and the quantity of sand needed to fill the Salton trough in California?

    Response: The quantity of sand that fills the Imperial Valley is roughly the same scale and type of sand weathered and eroded from the Grand Canyon and transported by the Colorado River and deposited in California.

Stability and Change
8. Phenomenon: It is harder to breathe when hiking at high elevation.

    Prompt: How does elevation affect the stability of the chemical processes that carry oxygen to your cells?

    Response: Changing the pressure of oxygen in the atmosphere changes the equilibrium conditions of the hemoglobin-oxygen interaction. Oxygen is a reactant in the reaction: $Hb(aq) + 4O_2$ (g) $\rightleftharpoons Hb(O_2) 4(aq)$, where "Hb" stands for hemoglobin. When there is less oxygen in the air, the equilibrium of the chemical reaction shifts toward the reactants and the hemoglobin carries less oxygen to the cells.

9. Phenomenon: The introduction of zebra mussels to the Finger Lakes of central New York State has changed the ecosystem.

    Prompt: How has the introduction of zebra mussels changed the living and nonliving parts of the Finger Lakes ecosystem?

    Response: The zebra mussels filtering phytoplankton has changed water clarity in the ecosystem. Increased water clarity allows light to penetrate further causing a rise in the population of aquatic plants. Increased light penetration causes water temperatures to rise and thermoclines to become deeper.

10. Phenomenon: In Hayward, California a curb and gutter have moved nearly a foot in the past 50 years.

    Prompt: How have changes to the Earth caused the curb and gutter to move?

    Response: Changes to Earth's surface are caused by the movement of tectonic plates. Earth's surface appears stable at short time scales but changes over longer time scales.

   Causality can be described in terms of the concepts of both cause and effect and structure and function relationships. Science seeks to find the causes of phenomena. When students understand causality, it helps them investigate cause and effect relationships or how the structure affects the way a system functions. We can think of causality as the causes or structures that lead to the effects or functions. It is sometimes useful for students to think about the phenomena as the effect or the function.

Examples for Causality

Cause and Effect

11. Phenomenon - Rivers and streams often meander across valleys in S-shaped patterns.

    Prompt: What causes the S-shaped patterns as rivers flow through valleys?

    Response: The speed of moving water is greater on the outside of the bend and slower on the inside of the bend. This causes sediment to erode from the outside bends and to deposit on the inside of the next bend downstream, causing the S-shaped pattern.

12. Phenomenon: The greater the height from which a rubber ball is dropped, the higher it bounces.

    Prompt: What causes the rubber ball to bounce higher when it is dropped from a greater height?

    Response: Dropping the ball from a greater height increases its potential energy. Increasing the potential energy increased the amount of kinetic energy the ball has when it bounces. This causes the ball to bounce higher.

Structure and Function

13. Phenomenon: Leaves have veins running throughout.

    Prompt: How does the structure of the veins in leaves function to meet the needs of the plant?

    Response: The structure of the veins in a leaf function to provide water to the leaf cells. The cells use sunlight to rearrange molecules of water and carbon dioxide into glucose. Plants store energy in the chemical bonds of glucose. The plant uses the glucose to store energy and as building blocks to construct larger molecules, such as cellulose, which are used to make the various parts of the plant.

14. Phenomenon: Shifting gears on a bicycle makes the ride more comfortable on hilly roads.

    Prompt: How does the structure of a bicycle provide a mechanical advantage to make climbing hills easier?

    Response: The structure of the sprockets and chain on a bicycle provides a way to vary the force needed to turn the wheels. The ratio of the number of sprockets on the front chainring and the number of sprockets on the rear chainring determine the amount of force needed to turn the wheel once.

Finally, students use **patterns** as evidence to support explanations for the causes of phenomena and/or to make predictions. Patterns help guide student thinking across all grade-levels as they make relevant observations and develop meaningful questions. In the early grades, observing patterns is central for students to develop the evidence needed to support explanations and arguments. In later grades, students analyze data to determine patterns and develop evidence of causal relationships. Across all grade levels, students use patterns as evidence to support explanations.

Examples for Patterns

Patterns

15. Phenomenon: When you look at snowflakes with a hand lens, the pattern of six-sided structures can be observed.

    Prompt: How does the structure of water molecules cause the six-sided pattern in snowflakes?

    Response: Snowflakes grow into familiar six-sided patterns as water molecules change from a liquid to a solid. The molecules line up based on the structure of water molecules and the electromagnetic attraction of the positive and negative ends of the water molecule.

16. Phenomenon: The moon appeared in the eastern sky about 50 minutes later today than yesterday.

    Prompt: What causes the pattern of moonrise and moonset?

    Response: Patterns in the motion of the sun, moon, and Earth cause predictable patterns of when objects appear in the sky. The Earth is spinning from west to east faster than the moon is orbiting from west to east. Because the moon is orbiting the Earth in the same direction as the Earth is spinning, it takes more than 24 hours to see the moon in the same position relative to a specific location on Earth.

17. Phenomenon: Deer mice in the Sandhills of Nebraska are tan; however, elsewhere in the state deer mice are dark brown.

    Prompt: How can we account for the pattern of differences in the color frequency of deer mice in Nebraska?

    Response: The pattern of increased frequency of tan fur color in deer mice in the Sandhills of Nebraska compared to mice on the surrounding prairie is evidence of natural selection of genetic traits for light fur color in the Sandhills. The light color provides an advantage for survival in the Sandhills but not elsewhere in Nebraska. The lighter color is more difficult for predators, such as owls and hawks, to see against the background of the light tan sand in the Sandhills.

Crosscutting Concepts can be used as lenses to help students see different aspects of the same phenomenon. Using multiple lenses in the investigation deepens student understanding of phenomena. For example, thinking about phenomena in terms of a system (i.e., stability and change; scale, proportion, and quantity; or energy and matter) helps students to understand the causes of the phenomena. Figure 3.3 shows a phenomenon, an event that is observable and for which there is a cause. Phenomenon — clouds sometimes appear in bands or waves. Students can investigate the causes of patterns in clouds using the lens of systems. More specifically, analyzing the flow of energy into and out of the system that causes matter to change can lead to deeper conceptual understanding. The explanation for this phenomenon may require the use of multiple crosscutting concepts to make sense of the changes in the system that cause the phenomenon.

The clouds and the surrounding air are interacting systems. The clouds are a system in which water, as a gas in the air, is moving with the air in a wave motion. As the particles of water gas move up in the atmosphere, energy is released to the colder surrounding air system, causing the water particles to condense into liquid water droplets. The liquid water droplets reflect light and the cloud is visible. When the wave

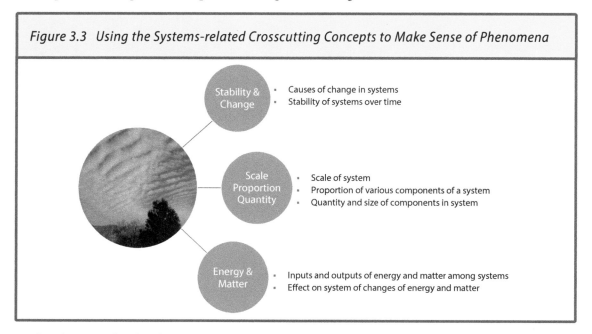

Figure 3.3 Using the Systems-related Crosscutting Concepts to Make Sense of Phenomena

Stability & Change
- Causes of change in systems
- Stability of systems over time

Scale Proportion Quantity
- Scale of system
- Proportion of various components of a system
- Quantity and size of components in system

Energy & Matter
- Inputs and outputs of energy and matter among systems
- Effect on system of changes of energy and matter

pushes the water droplets lower into the warmer part of the atmosphere, the increase in pressure and heat energy surrounding the cloud system transfers energy into the droplets causing the water to evaporate into water-gas that does not reflect light and thus is not visible. The water molecules are a system and the air surrounding the water molecules is a different system. Energy is flowing into and out of the water system. The proportion of water in the air determines if the phenomenon of visible cloud waves occurs; too much water and the cloud is continuous, too little water and we have blue skies. The system is changing as it moves, sometimes the system is stable, but only for a short time.

Multiple crosscutting concepts are needed to fully explain the appearance of clouds in wave formations. However, some phenomena may only need one crosscutting concept to effectively investigate causal relationships. Students become more proficient at using crosscutting concepts when teachers consistently and accurately use them to prompt student performances. The language of the crosscutting concepts should become touchstones across all science teaching and learning. Organizing the crosscutting concepts by function helps students to become proficient at using them.

Framing student performances with the crosscutting concepts support students' conceptual understanding of the natural and man-made world. Rather than thinking about topics such as plate tectonics, the human body, or ecosystems, teachers might focus on the crosscutting concepts (e.g., systems, energy and matter, stability and change, structure and function) to unify student reasoning and help them see coherence in science. Consistently prompting students with crosscutting concepts facilitates understanding of the function of these concepts across topics. Figure 3.4 provides examples of teacher prompts for the crosscutting concept of scale across different science topics. Keep in mind that scale concerns the size of things and the mathematic relationship among them. Framing class discussions about phenomena with crosscutting concepts facilitates a deeper understanding of the nature and appropriate use of each concept. Discussions about crosscutting concepts should occur during investigations of science phenomena and be consistent with the instructional model of engaging students in the phenomena first, prior to the class discussion.

Figure 3.4   Teacher Prompts Using Scale of Systems Across Multiple Science Topics

- How does the scale (mass) of the sun affect the interactions of the planets in the solar system?

- How does the scale (quantity) of cells in an organism affect the structure of the circulatory system?

- How does the scale (area) of a grassland ecosystem affect the stability of the ecosystem?

The utility of using crosscutting concepts becomes central to students' ability to **gather** meaningful data and information about systems and to **reason** the relationships between components of a system. As students develop a deeper understanding of the crosscutting concepts, they begin to use them to more effectively **communicate** their **reasoning**. It is important that teachers use crosscutting concepts to focus students on specific aspects of phenomena, but more important is for students to use crosscutting concepts to structure their responses. Figure 3.5 shows possible student responses to the above prompts.

Figure 3.5   Student Responses to Prompts Using Crosscutting Concepts Across Topics

- The scale of the sun is much larger than any other object in the solar system. It is over 98% of the mass of the solar system. This causes other objects to respond to the gravity of the sun. Planets that are much less than 1% of the mass of the sun are mostly affected by the gravity of the sun and very little by other planets.

- The human body has over 700 trillion cells. Each cell needs oxygen delivered and carbon dioxide removed. The circulatory system must have very fine branches to reach all these cells.

- Large scale ecosystems are more stable. Small ecosystems become less stable when predator numbers change and become out of balance with prey species. When the number of grazers is out of balance with the amount of grass in the ecosystem, overgrazing causes damage to the soil and less grass grows.

As familiar touchstones, crosscutting concepts build across disciplines and grade levels and contribute to students' sense of coherence in science learning. When students become proficient at using the crosscutting concepts, they become more effective at developing evidence for the causes of novel phenomena beyond the classroom.

Crosscutting Concepts and GRC

Crosscutting concepts are used in GRC instructional sequences to focus student performances and student and teacher questions during class discussions. Questions that use crosscutting concepts help students focus on specific aspects of phenomena that are germane to causal relationships. This is true both for the questions teachers and students use to direct investigations. One way to enhance the use of crosscutting concepts is to use them in couplets, pairs, or a series that link the phenomena to causal relationships or describe the system within which the phenomenon occurs. Coupling of crosscutting concepts helps focus students' attention on key aspects of a scientific phenomenon. The lesson prompts and questions teachers use to extend student thinking during class discussions are important opportunities for using couplets to direct student attention toward specific aspects of a phenomenon.

> *Crosscutting concepts serve as a lens to focus the science and engineering practices within student science performances.*

It is important that students learn how to transfer their knowledge of the crosscutting concepts to new contexts. When students use crosscutting concepts proficiently, with phenomena presented in the classroom, they are more effective at making sense of novel phenomena beyond the classroom. Students learn how to transfer knowledge of the crosscutting concepts when the teacher consistently and accurately engages them in using the concepts across a variety of phenomena (Moulding & Bybee, 2017).

Figure 3.6 Using Crosscutting Concepts to Prompt Student Responses

- How did the input of energy to the system cause changes in the system?
- How does the proportion of salt in the solution affect the transfer of water across the cell membrane?
- Why are some geological changes only observable on time scales of millions of years?
- Why does a pattern exist in the changes in numbers of some, but not all native species of birds when an invasive species is introduced into the ecosystem?
- What causes some fabric dyes to be stable and other dyes unstable when exposed to sunlight?
- How does the structure of the skeletal, muscular, and integumentary systems in a chicken foot function to help the chicken move and find food?

Pairing a science and engineering practice with crosscutting concepts is an effective way to direct student performances. When practices are coupled with crosscutting concepts, student performances are more strategically focused on specific causal aspects of the phenomenon. A performance such as, "Develop models to describe the flow of energy into and out of the system," is a way to focus students on how energy affects the system. Using the crosscutting concept *flow of energy* directs students to *develop models to describe* the movement of energy into, out of the system being investigated. The practices direct student performances, in this case, to develop a model, while the crosscutting concepts focus students on specific aspects of the system the model represents. Developing models that show the flow of energy from one system into another system engages students in three-dimensional performances.

Assessing Student Performances

Three-dimensional science performances are useful prompts for formative assessment. Science performance occurs when students engage in making sense of phenomena; however, when the three-dimensions are used to direct the performance, the teacher and student have a clearer understanding of the learning expectations. When practices are paired with crosscutting concepts in performances, student thinking is more clearly focused on specific aspects of scientific reasoning. Pairing practices with crosscutting concepts guide students in making thinking visible. This makes the crosscutting concepts an essential part of good formative assessment prompts.

Using crosscutting concepts to prompt students in formative and summative assessment is an efficient way to gather accurate evidence of student learning (CCSSO, 2018). Crosscutting concepts are an effective way to focus students' attention on specific aspects of phenomena in formative assessment for learning. Summative assessments often only engage students in using the practices and core ideas

without using the crosscutting concepts to focus students on specific aspects of a phenomenon. Using crosscutting concepts in summative assessment prompts, leads to a more accurate measure of student science proficiency. The crosscutting concepts, when used accurately and purposefully, are an effective way to direct students in three-dimensional science performances.

The following examples show how crosscutting concepts help focus students on specific aspects of a phenomenon. The examples in Figure 3.7 illustrate how using the crosscutting concepts can help teachers to direct student thinking toward important aspects of the phenomena for purposes of assessment.

Figure 3.7 Examples of Using Crosscutting Concepts to Help Students Focus on Specific Aspects of Phenomena

---

Phenomenon: The number of coyotes living in a desert ecosystem increases when the rabbit population increases.

Formative assessment questions:

Q-1 How do changes in the proportion of rabbits to coyotes affect the stability of an ecosystem?

Q-2 How are the coyote and rabbit populations related?

Identify the crosscutting concepts used in Q-1 and Q-2 and then reflect on (A) the role of crosscutting concepts in directing student thinking, and (B) what students need to know to answer each of these questions.

Phenomenon: When the number of rabbits in the desert increases, the amount of grass in the system decreases.

Formative assessment questions:

Q-3 How does the amount of rain affect the stability of the animal population in the desert ecosystem?

Q-4 Why is the amount of rain that falls in the desert important to the desert ecosystem?

Consider questions Q-3 and Q-4 and reflect on (A) the role of crosscutting concepts in directing student thinking, and (B) what do students need to know to answer each of the questions.

Science is a way of knowing based on evidence. Crosscutting concepts are a lens to focus on specific aspects of phenomena. However, several of the crosscutting concepts may also be used as evidence to support explanations; specifically, *matter is conserved, energy is conserved*, and *patterns*. Some of the crosscutting concepts help students investigate causal relationships, specifically, *cause and effect*, and *structure and function*. The balance of the crosscutting concepts direct students to gather evidence from specific aspects of systems to support explanations for the causes of changes.

1. Energy flows and matter cycles can be used by students as evidence to support explanations for the changes in systems. The concept that energy and matter are conserved is used to reason an explanation for the cause of movement of energy and/or matter among systems.

2. Patterns are often used as evidence in science. Patterns in data (observations and/or measurements) are used as evidence to support explanations for the causes of phenomena.

3. Cause and effect is a concept about the relationship between the phenomenon (effect) and its cause. In science, we seek evidence for the causes of phenomena. It is useful for students to think of the phenomena as the effect.

4. Structure and function is an underlying causal relationship that is useful for students to consider as evidence for how the structure of a system, organism, or engineered device functions to cause the observed phenomena.

5. Scale, proportion, and quantity are concepts we use to define systems and look for evidence of how the scale of the system, the proportions of components in the system, and the quantity of the components in systems affect the structure of the system and how the system performs.

6. Systems and system models are concepts that help us to define the boundaries and interactions among the systems or within a system. In science, we look for evidence that supports explanations for causes of changes within and among systems.

7. Stability and change are concepts that engage students in seeking evidence for how changing one component of a system causes changes to other components in a system. Changes occur at different time and size scales. Some changes are so slow or on such a small scale that they can be described as stable systems. Many phenomena are described as the observed changes and/or stability within or among systems. Investigations seek evidence for what causes systems to remain stable or change.

It is useful for students to use crosscutting concepts to gather evidence or direct the search for evidence. Crosscutting concepts support reasoning about the meaning of evidence or reasoning about the relationship of specific evidence to an explanation. Evidence developed from using these concepts helps students communicate reasoning about the causes of phenomena.

Core Ideas

Core ideas are scientific principles, laws, and aspects of theories that describe interactions of matter, energy, and forces in space and time. Core ideas are often presented at a much smaller grain size than theories. However, like theories and laws, core ideas have broad explanatory utility for students to make sense of myriad phenomena. The core ideas as described in the *Framework* progress across grade-levels and serve as a thread that students follow from the earliest grades through high school. Core ideas can also provide an organizational structure for the acquisition of new knowledge and are a key tool for understanding or investigating more complex ideas and solving problems (NRC, 2012). The progression of core ideas across grade-levels supports students' development of a conceptual understanding of science, as well as a set of examples and core ideas students can rely on as they build more sophisticated explanations in later grades.

Students use core ideas to make sense of phenomena. In the past, our learning expectation for science was for students to remember core ideas and recite them upon demand. Memorization, mnemonic devices, and songs were used to help students "memorize" core ideas. Science activities were focused on students trying to confirm or "prove" a theory, law, or core idea, or confirm an explanation that was provided prior to the activity. The new vision for science teaching and learning focuses on students using core ideas to construct explanations for phenomena rather than confirming the accuracy of these ideas.

Science instruction should engage students in using core ideas and crosscutting concepts to make sense of phenomena.

Multiple core ideas are generally needed to explain a single science phenomenon; conceptualizing core ideas helps students use them effectively. For example, Newton's laws of force and motion are usually taught in isolation and without connection to real-world phenomena. Applied to observable, natural phenomena, Newton's laws can be conceptualized and used to make sense of phenomena students encounter in the world.

Figure 3.8 Example of Student Thinking About Phenomena

Phenomenon: When I slammed a car door while standing on an icy driveway, my feet slipped, and I fell.

- Students don't think about this phenomenon as "For any pair of interacting objects, the force exerted by the first object on the second object is equal in strength to the force that the second object exerts on the first, but in the opposite direction (Newton's third law)" nor "The motion of an object is determined by the sum of the forces acting on it; if the total force on the object is not zero, its motion will change. The greater the mass of the object, the greater the force needed to achieve the same change in motion."

- Rather, students think about this phenomenon more like – "When I push an object it pushes back, and smooth surfaces provide a very small force (friction) to keep me in place."

The goal of science instruction is to have students use science concepts and ideas to make sense of phenomena. When observing a phenomenon such as a baseball thrown horizontally falling to Earth, the goal is for students to understand how the forces acting on the ball (horizontal force of the throw, vertical force of gravity, and force from collisions with air particles and the ball) causes changes in the motion of a ball, rather than merely having students state which of Newton's three laws explains the motion of a baseball. The "motion of an object is the result of the sum of the forces acting on the object" in this case is explained as a conceptualized core idea that includes multiple ways in which Newton's laws support explanations of this phenomenon, but also common student experiences beyond the classroom. Core ideas about friction, gravity, and motion are all part of making sense of the everyday phenomenon that "A baseball thrown horizontally will fall to Earth".

The *Framework* has limited the number of science ideas we expect students to learn. It describes these core ideas at an appropriate depth and sophistication for each grade-level. Unfortunately, too often we do not expect students to apply this limited set of ideas beyond the classroom. When students apply core ideas to make sense of phenomena beyond the classroom experience, they develop a deeper understanding of these ideas.

Figure 3.9 *Example of Conceptualized Core Ideas*	
PS2.A: FORCES AND MOTION – 8th Grade	Conceptualized Core Ideas
For any pair of interacting objects, the force exerted by the first object on the second object is equal in strength to the force that the second object exerts on the first but in the opposite direction (Newton's third law). The motion of an object is determined by the sum of the forces acting on it; if the total force on the object is not zero, its motion will change. The greater mass of the object, the greater the force needed to achieve the same change in motion. For any given object, a larger force causes a larger change in motion. Forces on an object can also change its shape or orientation. All positions of objects and the directions of forces and motions must be described in an arbitrarily chosen reference frame. (NRC, 2012, p. 115)	The motion of an object is the result of the sum of the forces acting on the object.

The greater the mass of a moving object, the greater the force it transfers in a collision.

Forces can change the shape or position of an object. |

One goal of science learning is for students to use knowledge about one phenomenon to make sense of many other, similar phenomena. This requires applying a small set of conceptualized core ideas and crosscutting concepts to make sense of an unlimited number of phenomena. In this book, we refer to phenomena with the same causes, but taking place in different contexts, as analogous phenomena. Since analogous phenomena have the same causes, students can use the same set of core ideas to support their explanations and arguments.

Examples of analogous phenomena include

a. Water appearing on the outside of a glass of iced water, clouds forming over a lake in the morning, eyeglasses fogging when leaving an air-conditioned building and walking outside, the bathroom mirror fogging up after a shower.

b. Large numbers of Mule Deer seen in the foothills of the Rocky Mountains during the winter, Canadian Geese fly south for the winter months and return north in the spring, Right whales migrate north in the spring as the days get longer.

c. Volcanoes are generally near coasts, the Rocky Mountains are one of only a few mountain ranges that are not near a coast, both the Atlantic and Pacific oceans have a mid-ocean volcanic ridge.

An important goal for science education is providing students with the skills to transfer knowledge to make sense of novel phenomena. Analogous phenomena provide opportunities for students to apply the science ideas and concepts learned in one investigation to make sense of similar, but novel phenomena beyond the classroom.

Conceptualizing core ideas is the basis for making sense of phenomena. A small set of core ideas can be used by students to make sense of many phenomena. Developing a cadre of familiar analogous phenomena helps students to conceptualize the most useful core ideas and apply them. Teachers can best cultivate students' understanding of core ideas by using familiar, local, and culturally relevant contexts for phenomena. Using relevant phenomena, those that students are likely to frequently encounter, develops students' interest and motivation to learn science. Utilizing phenomena in familiar contexts encourages students to look for other phenomena that are analogous to the ones presented in the classroom. Local phenomena help to leverage students' curiosity and develop a sustainable understanding of core ideas and create memorable examples students can apply beyond the classroom.

Understanding a science idea and using the words that represent that idea are two different entities. Adding language to ideas and concepts as students learn science is consistent with the nature of how students learn. Conversely, front-loading vocabulary is inconsistent with how students learn. We recommend students develop science language while engaged in investigations and not as a vocabulary list prior to the investigation. It is more efficient for students to learn science language (vocabulary) as they develop a conceptual understanding of the core ideas. Immersing students in the doing of science affords invaluable opportunities for students to deepen their knowledge of disciplinary core ideas in ways that go far beyond the memorization of facts, vocabulary, or the repetition of prescribed laboratory exercises (NASEM, 2019). Science language should be introduced after students have already engaged in using core ideas to make sense of phenomena. This approach provides students a way to apply new terminology into a meaningful context.

Constructing knowledge is about building on existing experiences. Words in context mean more than words out of context; we want students to learn the language of science while engaging in investigation of the causes of phenomena so the words are in context. Studying vocabulary lists and memorizing words are not an effective way to learn science. Effective strategies to organize knowledge into meaningful structures encourage learners to go beyond the explicit materials and to elaborate and enrich their mental representation of information by calling up and applying it in new contexts (NASEM, 2018). Once students have investigated a phenomenon and have a context for learning, the science language becomes meaningful. Generally students have learned the expected science language for a topic by the time they have completed an investigation.

Students in elementary, middle, and high school are unique, not just in age but also in sophistication and number of experiences they have had to understand increasingly abstract ideas. Instruction should consider how the progression of learning occurs across grades K-12. Each of the three dimensions has a clear progression that is considered as students engage in science and engineering performances. The ways we engage early grade students with phenomena may be the same as those that we use in later grades; however, the causal explanations we expect from students and the evidence they use to support their explanations are different. Older students have more experiences to support more sophisticated explanations. Figure 3.10 provides examples of student explanations for phenomena across grade-bands.

Phenomenon: Leaves are darker on the topside than on the bottom side.

Student questions: How does the structure of the leaf cause the top to be darker than the bottom? How are the cells near the top of the leaf different from the cells on the underside of the leaf? How would a leaf change if a light were placed under the leaf? How does the color of the leaf relate to the process of photosynthesis and cellular respiration?

Student performances
- Develop a model to show how parts of the leaf system interact with the environment and other parts of the plant to meet the needs of the plant system.
- Construct an explanation for how the structure of the leaf functions to meet the needs of the plant.
- Develop an argument for how the evidence you have gathered supports your explanation for how the structure of the leaf functions to meet the needs of the plant.

Causal relationships: The cells near the top of the leaf are more densely packed and have more chloroplasts, which contain green-colored chlorophyll inside the chloroplasts. The underside of the leaf has more loosely packed cells with fewer chloroplasts inside these cells.

The student explanation describes why the topside of a leaf has a greater number of chloroplasts causing it to appear a darker shade of green than the bottom side of the leaf. Chlorophyll is where carbon dioxide and water come together to make glucose needed by the plant system to function. This reaction is called photosynthesis.

The student arguments include that all collected leaves had darker topsides which serves as evidence that the top of a leaf has more chloroplasts, with more chlorophyll in them. Because the sun generally shines from above the plant, the leaves have evolved to have more chloroplasts where there is a greater amount of sunlight. The model of the leaf found on the website https://sketchfab.com/models/51899a9f8440427a83dd0a446a72e8fc shows that the structure of the palisades layer of the leaf is more densely packed and has more chloroplasts than the spongy layer on the underside of a leaf. This structure is consistent with how the leaf functions to produce sugars by photosynthesis. The veins in leaves bring water for photosynthesis to the cells in the palisades layer. Chlorophyll is where photosynthesis occurs. The function of the leaf is for photosynthesis-changing carbon dioxide and water into glucose in the presence of light. Based on information from reliable sources, there is a pattern of leaf color and environment. Plant leaves from tropical rainforests are relatively darker and more consistent in color than leaves from other climates. This is because the sunlight in rainforests is diffused and plants have evolved to take advantage of diffused sunlight by having more equal chloroplasts on both the top and bottomside of the leaf. Plants native to deserts have a considerable color difference between the top and bottom of the leaf. This is evidence that the intense sunlight is utilized by chloroplasts mostly on the top surface of the leaf. Plants native to dense forest areas tend to be larger and have darker green leaves. These plants use indirect sunlight in shadowy areas of the forest where there is little direct sunlight to maximize the photosynthesis.

The student models show 1) sunlight, 2) differences in the structure of the cells on the top and bottom of leaves, 3) and a balanced chemical reaction that shows carbon dioxide and water in the chloroplast reacting in the presence of light to produce glucose and oxygen.

In the examples provided in Figure 3.10, a learning progression is illustrated by the life science core ideas related to structure and function of living things in grades K-5, and then in combination with core ideas about cells and photosynthesis in the later grades. These ideas play out across four analogous phenomena and various crosscutting concepts (e.g., systems, structure and function, patterns) to help students develop an understanding of how the structures, shapes, and substructures of living organisms determine the functions needed to survive within an environment.

Lessons are grander than standards and have more science performances than appear in a single standard. Each standard is a single performance with one practice, one crosscutting concept, and one core idea. The standards were written to identify what should be assessed. Most standards rely on understanding multiple core ideas- although not explicitly stated - and multiple crosscutting concepts. GRC lessons have a series of performances with multiple practices, crosscutting concepts, and core ideas. Even within a single lesson performance, there may be more than one practices, core ideas, and crosscutting concepts.

Lessons provide a logical sequence of practices directed toward three-dimensional performances. These performances lead students from questions about phenomena to gathering data and information, developing models and constructing explanations for the causes of phenomena, and ultimately developing arguments that supports their explanation. Within the various parts of a lesson are a suite of practices that direct student reasoning (e.g., analyze data, evaluate information, construct explanations). The GRC model for lessons provides a structure for the sequence of practices that support students in gathering evidence, reasoning the causes of phenomena, and communicating the reasoning through writing, speaking, and/or developing models. Since most phenomena have complexcauses, lesson performances may address multiple core ideas. The core ideas are not always stated in the lesson performance expectations which require students to learn and use core ideas from 1) resources within the lesson, 2) apply core ideas previously learned, and 3) use core ideas learned in class discussions.

Sequences of GRC performances describe a series of three-dimensional performances applied across gather, reason, and communicate reasoning. An important characteristic of these sequences is that students gather data and information and use core ideas to reason and develop explanations for causes of phenomena. A common way students learn core ideas within lessons is by engaging in the practice of obtaining information about the causes of phenomena. Sometimes the information students obtain comes from the teacher during the class discussion as students synthesize core ideas into a conceptual understanding with appropriate science language. Learning core ideas in this way contributes to the overall breadth of examples of ways to apply core ideas to make sense of phenomena.

Science is a way of knowing based on evidence. Core ideas are used as evidence to support explanations. Many investigations function to help students seek evidence consistent with core ideas which leads to students using a core idea as part of the evidence that supports or refutes an explanation for the causes of phenomena as shown in the following example.

Phenomenon: Flat sheets of paper fall more slowly than wadded sheets of paper.

Explanation: When a flat and a wadded up piece of paper fall they experience the same gravitational force pulling the paper down. However, air is made of particles that are too small to see but that have mass. When the flat piece of paper falls it collides with more air particles than the wadded up piece of paper and thus experiences a greater upward force. The motion of an object is determined by the sum of the forces acting on it, which in both cases is the sum of the gravitational force pulling down and the forces exerted by air particles pushing up. So the flat piece of paper experiences a smaller net downward force and thus falls slower.

Note: See related lessons on the website *Going3DwithGRC* - 5th Grade 5-PS1-1 "Air is made of particles" and MS-PS2-1 "Air Force".

Students use investigations to gather evidence to support explanations. In this example, students might plan an experiment and develop a model to help them reason about causal relationships such as the effects of surface area on the rate a piece of paper falls. The experiment would most likely consist of students folding pieces of paper into smaller sizes (e.g., fold in half, fold in fourth, fold in eighth) and measuring the time it takes for the paper to fall to the floor. Students control the mass of the paper and the height from which the paper falls.

In this investigation, the focus is on gathering evidence to support the explanation that uses the core ideas: 1) matter (air) is made of particles too small to see; 2) the motion of an object is determined by the sum of the forces acting on the object; and 3) gravity is a force causing objects to fall to Earth. This is consistent with the *Framework*, which calls for students applying core ideas to support explanations of a variety of phenomena.

Core ideas are central to student explanations, whether students are using core ideas to support explanations or looking for evidence that is consistent with core ideas. In science, evidence is central to the way of knowing.

Core Ideas and Crosscutting Concepts Function in Similar Ways

Crosscutting concepts and core ideas function in similar ways within student science performances. Students use both the ideas and concepts to make sense of phenomena. Crosscutting concepts tend to be used to organize or focus student thinking. Both crosscutting concepts and core ideas are used within students' explanations for the causes of phenomena.

Combining multiple core ideas with couplets of crosscutting concepts helps students focus on specific aspects of the phenomena (e.g., matter is made of particles that have mass; motion of an object is the result of the sum of forces acting on objects; when energy is added to or taken away from matter, the properties of this matter changes; organisms that are best adapted to an environment tend to survive and reproduce to increase specific traits in a population). The building of core ideas and crosscutting concepts into conceptual models provides students with valuable tools to make sense of many phenomena within and beyond the classroom.

Students better understand one phenomenon when they begin to understand analogous phenomena operating in similar ways. Figure 3.11 is an example of how crosscutting concepts and core ideas work together to help students make sense of phenomena, and how an analogous phenomenon contributes to students' understanding of the initial phenomenon.

Figure 3.11 Phenomenon and Examples of Analogous Phenomena

Students use the crosscutting concepts of systems and transfer of energy in combination with the core idea of matter is made of particles and conceptualized core ideas energy is involved when matter changes to make sense of

1. why we get cold when wearing wet clothing on a windy day.

Then, applying the same crosscutting concepts and core ideas to make sense of

2. how sweating cools our bodies on a hot day.
3. why home evaporative cooling systems work better in the desert, then on the bayou.
4. why air temperatures are cooler near a lake.

Each of the analogous phenomena contributes significantly to students' understanding of the crosscutting concepts and core ideas. More importantly, they contribute to students' overall understanding of science and how to apply ideas and concepts across multiple phenomena. The capacity to conceptualize core ideas and apply them to make sense of novel phenomena is evidence of the learner's ability to transfer knowledge to new contexts.

We often hear students say, "This phenomenon is just like when…" and then describe an example of an analogous phenomenon. This is an important part of students' construction of knowledge. Operationalizing core ideas and crosscutting concepts as well as using analogous phenomena as examples help students develop conceptual models for scientific explanations. Using relevant examples helps students to construct new knowledge by building on existing experience, ideas, and concepts.

Summary - Crosscutting Concepts and Core Ideas

Science education has manifold goals, but perhaps the most important one is for students to enjoy learning science. Curiosity is one of the most important springboards for reaching this goal. Curiosity is an emotion that can be leveraged to support learning. Students can pursue their curiosity by using a set of core ideas and crosscutting concepts to make sense of phenomena they encounter in their lives. An important way for students to have a conceptual understanding of core ideas and crosscutting concepts is to connect learning experiences to locally and culturally relevant phenomena. Current learning theory supports the importance of connecting science learning to student experiences and prior knowledge. Instruction should not front-load select core ideas and crosscutting concepts but bring them to the forefront as students need them to make sense of a phenomenon. Deep understanding of core ideas and crosscutting concepts comes from learning these concepts and ideas within the context of applying them to make sense of analogous phenomena that students may encounter in their lives.

Science instruction consistent with the *Framework* engages students in using core ideas and crosscutting concepts to make sense of phenomena, not merely to remember or recite the ideas and concepts. Quality science assessment for student learning and assessment of student learning should provide evidence of students' ability to apply crosscutting concepts and core ideas to make sense of novel phenomena. Science assessments should look very much like science instruction. Assessments should engage students in three-dimensional performances in which students use core ideas and crosscutting concepts to construct explanations for the causes of novel analogous phenomena and argue how the evidence supports or refutes explanations.

Reflecting on Students Using Core Ideas and Crosscutting Concepts

Use the following prompts to initiate your reflections on Chapter 3.

1. How are crosscutting concepts different than core ideas?

2. Why is the use of couplets of crosscutting concepts more effective than using them in isolation?

3. Use Figure 3.7 as a guide and write a phenomenon and then two questions that use the crosscutting concepts to focus student reasoning about specific aspects of the phenomenon. How do students use core ideas to make sense of phenomena?

4. Why is it important for students to conceptualize core ideas rather than memorize them?

5. Reflect on strategies for prompting students to engage in science performances. How can crosscutting concepts be used to focus students on key aspects of a phenomenon?

6. Think of a simple phenomenon - now write a statement that uses crosscutting concepts to prompt students to make sense of this phenomenon.

7. How might using a GRC sequence be useful for assessing students' science knowledge?

References

Council of Chief State School Officers. (2018). *A primer for using crosscutting concepts to prompt student responses.* Available at https://ccsso.org/resource-library/using-crosscutting-concepts-prompt-student-reponses

Moulding, B., & Bybee, R. (2017). *Teaching science is phenomenal: Using phenomena to engage students in three-dimensional science performances consistent with the NRC framework and the NGSS.* Washington, UT: ELM Tree Publishing.

National Research Council. (2012). *A framework for k-12 science education: Practices, crosscutting concepts, and core ideas.* Washington, DC: The National Academies Press.

National Academies of Sciences, Engineering, and Medicine. (2018). *How people learn II: Learners, contexts, and cultures.* Washington, DC: The National Academies Press.

National Academies of Sciences, Engineering, and Medicine. (2019). *Science and engineering for grades 6-12: Investigation and design at the center.* Washington, DC: The National Academies Press.

Notes

Chapter 4
Building and Using GRC Lessons

TEACHERS use lessons as the basic unit of instruction. A lesson introduces the student to the learning expectations by activating prior knowledge and then providing new experiences to develop a deeper understanding of science and engineering practices, crosscutting concepts, and core ideas.

Lessons are the tool professional teachers use to guide instruction and record reflections for use in future instruction. Teachers make decisions about changes to lessons by reflecting on how students respond to instruction. The process of lesson development helps teachers to create new lessons and modify existing lessons to better understand the moving parts of instruction. While planning science instruction, educators generally have meaningful professional conversations with colleagues about teaching and learning. Professional educators enter into these conversations with the purpose of developing insights into how best to structure instruction to meet the needs of students. Lessons are blueprints to be modified and revised in response to student learning.

Generally, lessons are components of larger units that teachers have subdivided into smaller learning experiences that take a day or multiple days for students to complete. These smaller components should lead students to apply their learning from one phenomenon to make sense of other phenomena, deepening students' understanding. Lessons are most effective when they are connected to prior learning experiences and engage students in applying their knowledge to a new context. The set of smaller lesson components is most effective when aligned with larger learning goals.

The application of knowledge is an important goal for science learning and lessons should be developed to meet this goal. Investigation underpins science lessons and helps students learn by doing and applying knowledge to new contexts. Application of knowledge can best be facilitated by using analogous phenomena presented in new contexts, often within a single lesson to generalize ideas and concepts. During a lesson, the teacher and students use analogous phenomena to illustrate the concept or ideas, (e.g., blowing on a piece of paper causes it to move which is analogous to the way the wind causes a sailboat to move or running water causes a hydroelectric generator to spin.)

Investigations within the classroom provides students with the motivation, knowledge, and skills to make sense of phenomena beyond the classroom. This is the goal of all science education -- to equip students with the ability to make sense of the world around them. Figure 4.1 provides examples.

Figure 4.1 A Series of Lessons Leading to Students Applying Science Learning Beyond the Classroom	
In-Class Learning	Application of Learning Beyond the Classroom
▪ Students investigate the causes of the seasons and how the tilt of Earth causes the sun to appear in the southern sky.	▪ Emerson observes the full moon in the southern night sky and wonders about the causes, records observations in a journal, and applies learning about the sun and tilt of Earth. He applies his learning and develops a mental model for how the tilt of Earth causes the moon and planets to appear in the southern sky while the sun is in the north in the summer.
▪ Students investigate plate tectonics, weathering, and erosion using simulations and reading from the text.	▪ While on a driving vacation to a nearby state park, Elena observes a road cut and wonders why the rock layers are not all the same thickness. While at the state park visitors center, she asks a ranger about the geology of the park and she gives Elena a free brochure with information about the geology. When she arrives home, she gathers information from the internet about the geology of the area and develops an explanation for why that road cut had very different layers of rock, including a layer with fossils.
▪ Students investigate sexual and assexual reproduction in quaking aspen trees and raspberry plants. They learn that sexual reproduction results in greater genetic diversity.	▪ One early evening during the late summer, Jack observes swarms of flying ants. He goes to the internet to gather information from the Natural History Museum of London and learns that the ants are young females and males mating and starting a new ant colony. He applies his learning to understand why it is important for ants to mate with ants from other colonies.
▪ Students investigate how metals react with oxygen from the atmosphere to form metal oxides.	▪ When visiting her grandparents, Eva observes that the silver platter at their house has turned black. She applies her understanding of oxidation and shares with her grandmother why putting the platter in an airtight plastic bag would slow the tarnishing.

Rationale for Using GRC Lessons

The purpose of this chapter is to help teachers design lessons focused on 1) developing three-dimensional science performances, 2) engaging students in making sense of phenomena, and 3) structuring a sequence of student science performances in which students are gathering data and information, reasoning with the data and information to produce evidence, and communicating that reasoning. Gather, Reason, and Communicate Reasoning (GRC) is an instructional sequence that engages students in making sense of science phenomena. GRC lessons begin when students **gather** data, concepts, and ideas to **reason** the causes of phenomena, and then **communicate** this **reasoning**. The GRC is both a performance sequence for students and an instructional sequence for teachers. The GRC lessons described in this book and at the website *Going3DwithGRC*, are examples to help teachers design and use three-dimensional teaching and learning. The GRC template facilitates developing instructional sequences to deepen students' conceptual understanding of science learning consistent with the *NGSS* and state standards based on the *Framework*. Teaching for conceptual understanding is a primary goal for science education.

> *The GRC sequence helps build a positive learning environment and classroom culture for meaningful academic interaction among students.*

GRC lessons present a consistent structure for instruction. The sequence prompts students to 1) engage with a phenomenon; 2) gather data and information about the causes of the phenomenon to use as evidence and support reasoning; 3) evaluate information and analyze and interpret data to use for constructing explanations and developing arguments, and models; 4) communicate reasoning through writing, speaking, and models; and 5) engage in making sense of analogous phenomena beyond the class-

room. Throughout this instructional sequence, the science performances of the students are supported by the actions of the teachers during instruction.

The process for GRC lesson development is a straightforward approach for planning instruction built on students' inquisitiveness and curiosity. Using GRC lessons helps students become active members of a classroom science community and take ownership of their science learning. This sequence helps build a positive learning environment and classroom culture for meaningful academic interaction among students. Figure 4.2 describes how teachers guide student performances across the components of the GRC instructional sequence.

Sequence	Student Performance	Teacher Guidance
	Figure 4.2 *Teacher Guidance for Supporting Students in Science Investigation and Engineering Design*	
Gather	<ul><li>Explore phenomena.</li><li>Ask questions about phenomena.</li><li>Make relevant observations.</li><li>Plan and carry out investigations to gather data and obtain information to make sense of phenomena.</li></ul>	<ul><li>Present phenomena in ways that pique student curiosity and motivate learning.</li><li>Support students in developing relevant questions.</li><li>Facilitate students making connections among core ideas and crosscutting concepts related to the phenomena.</li></ul>
Reason	<ul><li>Analyze and interpret data and evaluate information to use as evidence.</li><li>Develop models, construct explanations, and develop arguments for how the evidence supports or refutes explanations for the causes of phenomena.</li></ul>	<ul><li>Set clear expectations that student use evidence to support their explanations and argue the merit of each line of evidence for the explanation.</li><li>Help students to develop skills to analyze data.</li></ul>
Communicate Reasoning	<ul><li>Write, speak, and use models to communicate reasoning about the causes of phenomena.</li><li>Reflect on their own artifacts of learning.</li></ul>	<ul><li>Carefully read student writing and provide meaningful feedback about their use of evidence to support reasoning.</li><li>Establish multiple opportunities for students to produce and revise models and explanations that communicate their reasoning.</li><li>Reflect on student learning and consider ways to improve instruction.</li></ul>
Apply Beyond the Classroom	<ul><li>Use three-dimensional learning to make sense of analogous phenomena in the world beyond the classroom.</li></ul>	<ul><li>Plan coherent support for students to connect learning to analogous phenomena beyond the classroom.</li></ul>

Adapted from *Science and Engineering for Grades 6-12: Investigation and Design at the Center* (NASEM, 2019)

Key attributes of GRC lessons include

1. A series of coherent science performances to support students in generating evidence for the causes of phenomena;

2. A set of teaching suggestions to support teachers in implementing instruction;

3. Key questions to initiate classroom discussion and help students make their thinking visible;

4. A clear description of assessment for student learning (formative) enabling teachers to interpret and act on evidence of student learning;

5. Sets of science essentials that describe observable student performances for practices, core ideas, and crosscutting concepts;

6. A sequence of science practices across GRC to prompt student performances at each stage of the lesson; and

7. Embedded formative assessments for learning.

Over the course of many years, we have found the use of the GRC sequence to be an intentional and thoughtful process for improving instruction and classroom practice in which students are at the center. The power of GRC lessons resides in reflecting on and thinking about the needs of students. Teachers report significant changes in their instruction:

"Students have responded very well and as you said I am igniting that curiosity! Thank you for helping me find the justification I needed to step aside from my previous teaching."

"GRC has changed my instruction, I now teach from the heart, not from the book."

"Finally, students have something to write about!"

"Everywhere I go I see phenomena; it makes my life more interesting!"

"Students love bringing phenomena to class to share."

"GRC lessons produce memorable learning for all students."

Instructional Design Builds Across a Series of Student Performances

Arguably the most important innovation in the *Framework* and *NGSS* is the use of the three-dimensions in each of the standards. GRC lessons support this innovation by organizing what students do (practices), into a sequence that leads students from gathering data and information to using the data and information as evidence to support explanations and finally on to communicating that reasoning. GRC is an instructional sequence as well as a strategy for students to make sense of phenomena. Making sense of phenomena and designing solutions for problems helps to motivate teaching and learning in each GRC lesson. The GRC instructional sequence is a powerful instructional structure supported by research to tackle three-dimensional teaching and learning as described in the *Framework* and *NGSS* (NASEM, 2019).

Developing GRC lessons helps teachers organize complexity and maintain the integrity of three-dimensional science learning. The GRC instructional sequence provides a structure for students to develop conceptual understanding around an idea. It is in contrast to the abstract, often meaningless lab activities for which students find an answer to what happens but rarely come to understand why. GRC lessons make the transition to implementing standards more about personal reflections as a professional educator while putting forward the spirit of the innovations. GRC lessons often span a sequence of multiple days in which students are introduced to the phenomenon and subsequently gather more data and information, make sense of and reason with that data and information, and communicate reasoning supported by evidence.

Teaching is about empowering students to learn beyond the classroom. GRC lessons provide a process for students to discover knowledge by observing phenomena and pursuing meaningful questions about the causes. Students participate in dialogues from positions of knowledge and develop explanations based on evidence. Mortimer Adler (1982) asserted that learning by discovery occurs when teachers coach students and thrust them into situations in which they have to observe, measure, and classify, as opposed to attempting to put the knowledge of the teacher into the mind of the students. Engaging students in science learning by using GRC helps them take ownership of their learning, as curiosity and inquisitiveness become the motivators of learning.

The GRC lesson sequence focuses students on a series of three-dimensional performances that lead them to reason about phenomena and then communicate that reasoning. The sequence has utility for organizing instruction and provides a structure for students to make sense of science phenomena. Teachers who develop GRC lessons discover that reflection on teaching and learning is a valuable by-product of the process. For students, the GRC is about using practices, core ideas, and crosscutting concepts to reason the evidence supporting the causes of phenomena.

Science instruction should engage students in meaningful investigations. Investigations seek evidence to support explanations for the causes of phenomena. The evidence is gathered by students using practices and comes from multiple sources (e.g., experiments, core ideas, crosscutting concepts, infor-

mation from valid/reliable sources). Investigations should provide opportunities for students to 1) ask and pursue the questions they ask; 2) reason the relationships between explanation and evidence; 3) present arguments for how the gathered evidence supports their explanations; and 4) become sufficiently curious to pursue science beyond the classroom. Science instruction is guided by lessons. The GRC lessons, which teachers develop and use for science instruction, intentionally engage students in meaningful investigations.

The GRC lesson structure organizes instruction in lessons and changes the way teachers think about the classroom culture and their pedagogical choices. Teachers can structure their instruction in a systematic way while maintaining ownership of teaching and learning using the GRC. The teacher is responsible for making instructional decisions that affect student learning. We encourage you to use the GRC structure to guide your reflection on teaching and learning.

Developing and Using the GRC Sequence to Engage Students in Doing Science

Science teaching is about designing learning experiences that motivate and support students as they construct explanations for the causes of phenomena. The context of science investigations affects students' interest in learning. Lessons that are relevant include contexts (e.g., sports, music, environment) of interest to students. The Framework reminds us that the world is about conceptual understanding, not factual details. The goal is not learning the three dimensions rather, using the three dimensions to learn about the world. GRC lessons are designed to engage students in using the three dimensions to make sense of phenomena in their world.

The **Gather** component helps students obtain the data and information to fuel reasoning. Questions are an important part of the gathering process; students ask questions about the phenomena they encounter. Student questions are then refined and developed to either plan an investigation or obtain pertinent information from reliable sources. The investigations yield data that is used as evidence and the sources provide information that is used for reasoning. During the investigation, students analyze data to find patterns and organize information. The gathering performances provide opportunities for meaningful integration of reading, listening, writing, and speaking within science.

The **Reason** component requires students to think about the relationships among evidence and explanation. Students enter the reasoning component of the sequence with data and information from the gathering portion of the investigation. However, in order for this data to become evidence, it must be analyzed, interpreted, and evaluated for relevance. Students can use this evidence to reason relationships that are then used for explanations and models. Another way for students to reason relationships is to develop and use models (e.g., equations, graphs, formulas) to reason relationships and find relevant patterns among data to use as evidence. They are then able to develop arguments for how the evidence supports the explanations and/or models. Finally, students can use core ideas and crosscutting concepts as an additional line of evidence to support their explanations with arguments. Throughout the reasoning process, students engage in productive and respectful discourse with peers as they reflect on their learning in the process of constructing explanations and arguments. Reasoning, that is seeking an explanation for the causes of phenomena, should be at the center of any GRC science lesson.

Communicating Reasoning is essential for science teaching and learning. Students communicate their reasoning by presenting a thoughtful explanation for the causes of a phenomenon, or by arguing how the evidence they have gathered supports or refutes an explanation. Students use models, writing, and oral communication to share their reasoning and make thinking visible (NRC, 2008). Communicating reasoning provides an opportunity for students to evaluate their own reasoning and determine if they have sufficient evidence to support an explanation. This reflection often prompts students to seek additional supporting evidence, emulating the work of scientists.

The GRC sequence benefits teachers and students on many levels. It provides an intentional and organized structure for teaching and learning. The lessons help teachers engage students with phenomena in ways that students become curious and invested in learning. Students benefit from having an orderly and consistent way to investigate new phenomena. Learners tend to persist in learning when they see the value and utility of what they are learning (NASEM, 2018).

Formative Assessment for Student Learning in GRC Lessons

There are multiple opportunities to collect evidence of student learning. Assessment is the process of collecting evidence of students' acquired knowledge and their ability to use that new understanding. Formative assessments can be *formal* — a record of proficiency for each student on key outcomes that guide future instruction, or *informal*—observations of students that can be used to immediately guide instruction. Each of the components of the GRC has measurable performances of student learning. The gathering component of the lessons provides opportunities for *informal* formative assessments. Examples of these opportunities include the quality of the student questions, the plan for the investigation, the data that is collected, and the models to organize data and information to seek patterns.

The reasoning component of the GRC lesson provides meaningful opportunities for both *informal* and *formal* formative assessment. The performances can be used to assess students' ability to analyze data, evaluate information, use models to reason the relationship among variables and parts of a system, and use evidence to support explanations or argue for how the evidence supports an explanation. Class discussion is typically in the reasoning component of a GRC lesson and creates some of the best opportunities for informal formative assessment. The questions in these discussions should be well planned and framed using crosscutting concepts to yield the best insights into student reasoning. Class discussions are often followed with performances in which students revise their explanations, models, or arguments.

The communicate reasoning component of the GRC lesson typically requires individual performances that can be used as either formal formative assessment **for** student learning or summative assessment **of** student learning. Both formative and summative assessments function to guide instruction and advance student knowledge and skill in three-dimensional learning. The communicate reasoning performances are most often explanations, models, or arguments. GRC lessons include rubrics and other assessment tools to use in the communicate reasoning performances portion of the lesson.

Ongoing embedded assessments benefit both the student and teacher. Students benefit by having opportunities to reflect on and adjust their own learning and receiving feedback from peers and the teacher. Teachers benefit by obtaining evidence of learning to inform changes to instruction. The GRC lessons have assessments that include suggestions for how teachers might "act on the evidence from assessments" to add instructional adjustments that extend or remediate the instruction.

Achieving the *Framework's* vision for science teaching and learning requires assessing three-dimensional performances holistically. Formative assessment for learning informs instruction by helping teachers measure student progress, determine the next steps for supporting learning, evaluate learning, and provide evidence for learning. Equally important is for students to gain insights into their own learning

Chapter 5

Administrator Support for GRC Lessons

SCIENCE STANDARDS provide an opportunity to improve teaching and learning — not because of the standards alone, but because they provide momentum for changing instruction. Administrators play a critical role in supporting teachers in making meaningful instructional changes. Administrators who understand three-dimensional science standards and the GRC instructional sequence can effectively facilitate professional dialogue that has positive impacts on instructional changes. This chapter outlines ideas and actions administrators can take to support teachers in making substantive improvements in science teaching and learning.

Supporting Teachers in Planning and Teaching GRC Lessons

The school principal is the individual in most educational systems responsible for instructional leadership. Principals oversee and supervise teachers, inspiring them as professional educators to develop the skills, dispositions, and knowledge to provide effective instruction that is sound in both practice and theory. Administrators support reflective teaching practice by facilitating discussions, typically about what the teacher does to initiate three-dimensional student science performances and how students respond. Within GRC, this is considered a teaching and learning interaction.

Instructional transformation is challenging and requires teachers to take risks as they move out of their instructional comfort zone. Meaningful and sustained instructional transformation occurs in school cultures that support innovation. This includes providing teachers with the time, resources, and professional development to improve instruction. Administrative leadership greatly influences the instructional transformation around science instruction using GRC.

Each teacher ultimately decides what and how to teach in his or her classroom, but this decision is influenced by decisions at other levels of the system. First, there is the effect of decisions made at the school level, which include the setting of expectations and sequences in certain content areas, as well as the principal's, department chairs', or team leaders' explicit and implicit signals about teaching and learning priorities. Leaders at the school level may also make decisions about the time and resources allocated to different subjects within guidelines and requirements set by the state. The hiring of teachers, instructional assignments, and the school building facilities and space for science can all influence the ability of a teacher to engage in successful science teaching. The principals' expectations, priorities, and decisions

 establish a climate that encourages or discourages particular pedagogical approaches and collegial interactions. Moreover, a school's degree of commitment to equity—providing opportunities for all students to learn the same core content—can influence which teachers are hired, how they are assigned to teach particular classes, how students are scheduled into classes, and how instructional resources are identified and allocated.

An administrator's first step in supporting teachers using the GRC instructional sequence is a commitment to implementing standards consistent with the *Framework* and/or *NGSS*. This may mean connecting desired changes in science with existing work to improve teaching and learning in English language arts and mathematics. Perhaps it is determining the best science professional development for three-dimensional teaching and learning, and then providing support for teachers and administrators to access it.

Effective professional development models a student-centered approach that engages educators in science experiences similar to those expected in classroom instruction. When possible, administrators should participate in professional development alongside their teachers. This provides a shared understanding of the new vision and necessary time to engage with and reflect on how GRC lessons structure thinking around three-dimensional science performances. Teachers and administrators working together and reflecting on how to best teach science are a powerful means to internalize and sustain transformation. This provides coherence and continuity of focus.

Quality Science Teaching and Learning

The foundation of the GRC learning sequence is based upon constructivist learning theory which states that students build knowledge based on experiences. The constructivist perspective emphasizes prior knowledge and challenges established institutionalized beliefs. Shapiro (1994) asserted that believing that knowledge is constructed by the learner guides educators in the presentation of experiences that support the learner's role in making knowledge their own. Scientific knowledge, therefore, builds on the publicly accepted constructions of ideas about events and phenomena.

When teachers use an instructional sequence such as the GRC, instruction is different than traditional approaches. This does not mean administrators need to abandon current professional performance review criteria used within the district or school. It is difficult for principals to possess a deep understanding of every curricular area and it is unreasonable for them to have a different review criterion for each discipline. We recommend teachers and principals work together as professional educators around a common language discussing high-quality instruction and how classroom practice is improved by using the GRC instructional sequence.

Classroom observation is an important part of professional learning. It is useful for the teacher and observer to prepare for a classroom visit by discussing the intended teaching and learning, and the lesson being used to reach those goals. Prior to any classroom observation, the GRC lesson being taught should be shared with the observer. We recommend the teacher print the GRC lesson and write a few notes to help the observer follow the instructional sequence and highlight the learning goals.. We encourage the teacher and observer to take time prior to the observation to discuss the learning goals, the phenomenon in the lesson, and instructional strategies being used. A clear set of learning goals should be established and related to students using core ideas and crosscutting concepts to make sense of phenomena. Teachers should remind administrators that GRC lessons often extend beyond the traditional 45-minute class period and share how the day's instruction will be connected to the next episode of learning. The post-observation interview is an opportune time for a discussion about how the students responded to the lesson. This is an important time for reflection and discussion of the successful aspects of the instructional episode. The teachers should view this as a time to describe how future instruction should proceed.

A single classroom observation is unlikely to include the entire GRC lesson sequence, which may last several days. This is one reason why coherence across the instructional sequence is an important part of quality instruction. Coherence in lessons comes from science performances leading to students 1) gathering information and data to use as evidence, 2) reasoning with the evidence to construct explanations for the causes of phenomena, and 3) using models and artifacts to communicate their reasoning. The lesson plan is a useful way for the teacher to communicate to the administrator the scope of the instruction.

The lesson plan helps the administrator to 1) recognize anticipated interactions among the teacher and students, 2) identify the intent of instruction and the instructional strategies the teacher brings to the lesson, 3) identify where the teacher differentiates instruction to meet the needs of students, and 4) recognize the purposes for the class discussion and how the teacher prompts students to ask questions. GRC lesson plans act as blueprints for instruction. Master teachers are effective at modifying the lesson to meet individual student needs and/or leveraging teaching moments that arise from students during the sequence of performances and class discussion.

A Protocol for Observing Science Teaching and Learning

A single instructional observational tool cannot capture all of the nuances of classroom instruction. The Partnership for Effective Science Teaching and Learning (PESTL) developed the PESTL Observation Protocol for Science (POPs) shown in Figure 5.1, as a tool to observe and document instructional changes as a result of professional development. POPs is useful for observing changes from traditional learning to instruction that engages students in three-dimensional performances. We do not advocate that you change your existing observation tools, but we do believe reviewing the POPs will provide insights into the attributes of quality science instruction. You may find meaningful connections between POPs and your existing observation tools.

The central focus of GRC lessons is for students to gather, reason, and communicate their reasoning; hence, the POPs observation tool is organized around these components. The POPs tool measures how well students engage in the practices and use crosscutting concepts and core ideas. The POPs help to focus the observation on students engaged in science investigations. Administrators should seek to find evidence during the observation of students reasoning in the investigation and investigating for a reason.

POPs provides a three-point scale rubric that can be used as an observation protocol with the GRC instructional sequence. The POPs should be viewed as a teaching and learning interaction because it describes teacher actions and how students respond to these actions or prompts. A key point to emphasize is this *process* is focused on three-dimensional student performances and the *product* is three-dimensional learning. If one observes students "doing science," this may only include one dimension instead of the three-dimensional student science performances which are inherent in the GRC instructional sequence.

Administrators have found the abbreviated version of the POPs protocol to be useful for structuring discussions with science teachers about ways to improve science teaching and learning. The instrument can be used to structure discussions among teachers in professional learning communities (PLCs). More details on using the POPs in PLCs can be found in Essay E in Chapter 6. Below is the abbreviated POPs instrument.

The following rubric is used as the criteria for analyzing interactions of teaching and learning within an instructional episode. The letters "a" through the letter "s" are the indicators to be observed. Only the indicators present in the teaching and learning episode are analyzed since the observation is for the purpose of initiating a discussion, not evaluation.

3 – Student performance observed is consistent with the description of the indicator. The performance provides clear evidence to the observer that the students are engaged in meaningful and memorable science learning that is likely to transfer to making sense of analogous phenomena beyond the classroom.

2 – Student performance observed is consistent with the description in the indicator. The performance provides evidence to the observer that students are engaged in meaningful science that may or may not transfer to making sense of analogous phenomena.

1 – Student performance observed was not fully consistent with the indicator. The performance was disjointed and did not focus on the intent of the indicator. The students were engaged in meaningful science.

0 – Student performance observed was not consistent with the intent of the indicator. The performance was disjointed and not the focus of instruction. The instruction was teacher-centered and students did not engage in performances beyond taking notes. Students participated in an activity not connected to scientific evidence, and/or reading materials were not connected to phenomena.

Figure 5.1 PESTL Observation Protocol for Science (POPs) : A Tool for Observing Three-Dimensional Teaching and Learning	
Gathering Performances	Descriptors for Reflection
Asking and Developing Questions/Obtaining Information	
a. The **teacher** uses a phenomenon to engage students in 1) developing questions and/or 2) obtaining information and extends students thinking about scientific phenomena in ways that lead to **students** asking questions and obtaining data, information and/or clarifying ideas.	How and why questions are used by teacher and students. How would we learn more about the phenomenon? Score: ___/3
b. The **teacher** uses crosscutting concepts to frame student expectations. **Students** use crosscutting concepts to ask their own questions, structure responses to others' questions, obtain information, and/or to clarify or extend others' questions.	What causes changes in the system? How are patterns related to the changes in the system? Score: ___/3
c. The **teacher** creates opportunities for students to connect their background experiences, previous learning, and core ideas from similar phenomena to the phenomenon being investigated. The **teacher** uses accurate language to conceptualize core ideas in discussions and actively extends students' thinking of science ideas during the discussion. **Students** accurately obtain information and connect core ideas and conceptual models from similar phenomena to the phenomenon being investigated and discussed.	Core ideas are presented in conceptual ways. Students accurately connect the phenomenon under investigation to appropriate core ideas or experiences from similar phenomena and/or experiences. Score: ___/3
Planning and Carrying Out Investigations	
d. The **teacher** engages students through an investigation of phenomena to obtain information and extend student thinking. **Students** investigate phenomena through gathering data/information and/or evidence.	A safe environment is created for students to investigate phenomena. Students gather data or information to use as evidence. Score: ___/3
e. The teacher and students describe and/or define phenomena under investigation in terms of systems and causality, and students seek patterns in data from investigations.	Change, matter and energy, scale-proportion-quantity, and patterns are central to the investigation. Students seek patterns to use as evidence. Score: ___/3
Gathering Reflections (comments here)	

During the observation of the gathering component of the lesson, many of the interactions are only observable among students in small groups. The observer gathers evidence of learning by listening in on small group discussions.

Figure 5.1 PESTL Observation Protocol for Science (POPs) : A Tool for Observing Three-Dimensional Teaching and Learning (continued)		
	Reasoning Performances	

Using Models

f.	The **teacher** uses models to support student structures for reasoning about phenomena. **Students** use models to help organize reasoning about phenomena and/or make predictions.	Models are used to reason about relationships. Students are expected to make predictions for the causes of the phenomenon. Score: ___/3
g.	The **students** use models to reason about interactions among the components of systems and/or cause and effect relationships for changes in systems. **Students** use models to develop evidence, seek patterns, and/or make predictions about the causes of changes in systems.	Students use models to establish relationships among the components of the system. Students seek patterns observed and use the patterns as evidence to make predictions. Score: ___/3

Constructing Explanations

h.	The **teacher** establishes clear expectations for students to construct explanations. **Students** construct explanations supported by evidence for the causes of phenomena.	Instruction creates a structure for students to develop evidence through reasoning. Score: ___/3
i.	The **teacher** establishes the expectation for students to develop explanations for causes of phenomena. **Students** use evidence to support explanations for the causes of changes in systems.	Causes of the phenomenon are explained using patterns as evidence. Score: ___/3
j.	The **students** use core ideas as evidence to support explanations for the causes of phenomena.	Core Ideas are used as evidence in explanations. Score: ___/3

Developing Arguments

k.	The **teacher** establishes a classroom environment and expectations for students to support assertions with evidence and reasoning. **Students** use data, information, patterns, and core ideas as evidence to support arguments for the causes of phenomena.	Students engage in developing arguments for how the evidence supports an explanation. Score: ___/3
l.	The **teacher** establishes the expectation for students to argue how or why the evidence supports the causes of changes in systems for the phenomenon. Students develop arguments for how or why data/evidence/ideas support explanations for causes of changes in systems and/or phenomena.	Arguments should focus on the causes of the phenomenon and be described in terms of the system and changes in the system. Score: ___/3
m.	The **students** use appropriate core ideas to support arguments.	Accurate core ideas are used to support arguments. Score: ___/3
	Reasoning - Reflection (comments here)	

Observing reasoning is challenging because you are looking for evidence of student thinking. Most reasoning is observed in class discussions, small group discussions, or when students begin to develop models and communicate reasoning. Learning occurs in no specific order and in ways that may be difficult to observe directly.

The communicate reasoning section of the protocol is seeking evidence of student reasoning through writing, speaking, or developing models. The expectation for all GRC lessons is that all students make their thinking visible. The lesson may extend beyond one class period and the student's reasoning becomes more clearly visible during the formal individual student performances at the end of the lesson.

Figure 5.1 PESTL Observation Protocol for Science (POPs) : A Tool for Observing Three-Dimensional Teaching and Learning (continued)	
Communicate Reasoning Performances	
Present Arguments Supported by Evidence	
n. The **teacher** engages students in presenting arguments supported by evidence for the causes of phenomena. **Students** present arguments for how or why the evidence supports their explanation or claim.	The teacher creates opportunities for students to share arguments through speaking or writing. Score: ___/3
o. The **students** present arguments for how data/evidence/core ideas support explanations of the causes of changes in systems and/or causes of phenomena. **Students** use evidence to support arguments for the causes of changes in the system in terms of inputs of matter and energy.	Students use evidence of patterns to support reasoning and explanations. Score: ___/3
p. The **teacher** establishes clear expectations that students develop arguments that use core ideas as evidence to support explanations. Students present arguments that accurately use core ideas as evidence to support explanations.	Lesson prompts describe the use of core ideas in performances. Students use the core ideas to support their arguments for the causes of phenomena. Score: ___/3
Use Models to Present Evidence and/or Explanations	
q. The **teacher** expects students to use models to communicate explanations. **Students** use models to communicate explanations.	Teacher expects students to use models when communicating reasoning. Score: ___/3
r. The **teacher** expects students to use models of systems. **Students** describe interactions of matter, energy, and forces in systems.	Students' models trace the flow of energy and/or matter in systems. Score: ___/3
s. The **students** use models to communicate core ideas to support explanations for the causes of phenomena.	Students use models to communicate explanations (causes and/or mechanisms) and/or arguments. Score: ___/3
Communicate Reasoning - Reflection (comments here)	

An important aspect of classroom observation is the observer and teacher each reflect on the teaching and learning that occurred during the lesson. This reflection should include a discussion focused on lesson structure, how teachers prompted students, and student responses during the episode. Less emphasis should be placed on the instruction that should have happened. Being told "you should have" is not a productive way to initiate reflection. Discussing what happened and teacher plans for future instruction are more productive in causing instructional improvements. When the POPs is used to guide the observation, the discussion is naturally focused on the teaching and learning paired interactions; what the teacher does and how the students respond. The reflection should include reviewing the lesson instructional sequence of gathering, reasoning, and communicating reasoning. Often the full GRC sequence does not happen within the timeframe of the observation but should be discussed as part of the instructional plan.

Teachers being observed for annual review or evaluation of teacher effectiveness perform well when using GRC lesson plans. We do not advocate schools/districts change their observation protocol; however, we do advocate that you consider how GRC approaches to teaching and learning can be judged for quality, fidelity, and efficacy using your existing tools for classroom observation.

The POPs is a useful catalyst for reflecting on classroom teaching and learning. Administrators may wish to use the POPs to provide practical and constructive feedback to teachers. Teachers can use the POPs as a vehicle for reflecting on effective three-dimensional science teaching and learning.

Summary – Administrator Support for GRC Lessons

Successful science teaching and learning occurs when teachers are inspired to improve instruction. The GRC lesson ideas provide teachers with a useful structure for engaging students in meaningful science learning. Administrators have an important role in inspiring and supporting teachers in instructional

changes that focus on three-dimensional student learning. An important part of instructional improvement are teachers making intentional changes consistent with how students learn. When teachers know how instructional changes affect learning and why they are making specific changes, they are more likely to be successful at improving teaching and learning. The GRC is an example of an instructional structure that organizes student performances and teaching strategies into a meaningful sequence.

Effective professional development should model the three-dimensional science instruction we expect our teachers to use with their students (CSSS, 2018). Reflection on teaching and learning with colleagues and/or administrators is essential for teachers to sustain instructional improvement. The most important professional learning occurs when teachers apply it to their own instructional practice and reflect on student learning. Reflection is an integral part of professional learning.

Teachers need time to learn, meet, and reflect. This involves the development of communities of professional learners. These communities may be as small as two teachers or in a large department. This professional learning can be accomplished by in-person discussions and lesson study, virtual dialogues, lesson development, and/or self-reflection and journal writing. Instructional changes take time for teachers to digest and put into practice the innovations of the GRC lesson sequence. The goal is to improve student learning, the mechanism is for teachers to internalize and implement instructional improvements.

Structural and logistical support is the responsibility of administrators. Administrators should support teachers in developing a clear understanding of three-dimensional science performances. These performances are a mechanism for student learning. The GRC lessons are consistent with the vision for science teaching and learning described in the *Framework*. The innovations for instruction needed to implement the three-dimensional science standards are consistent with 1) the goals of science education, 2) constructivist learning theory, and 3) the instructional strategies that engage students in science performances. The GRC lessons are consistent with and help teachers implement these innovations.

Reflecting on Administrator Support for GRC Lessons

Use the following prompts to initiate your reflections on Chapter 5.

1. How can administrators best support teachers in implementing the GRC instructional sequence?

2. How can classroom discourse be improved to more effectively support the teaching and learning process?

3. It is unlikely your school system uses the POPs to observe teachers, so how can you incorporate elements from the POPs to inspire instructional improvements?

4. Why is it important to view teaching and learning as a paired interaction?

5. Why is reflection an important part of the instructional change process?

References

Council of State Science Supervisors. (2018). *Science professional learning standards.* Available at http://cosss.org/Professional-Learning

Shapiro, B.L. (1994). *What children bring to light: A constructivist perspective on children's learning in science.* Teachers College Press: New York, New York.

Notes

Chapter 6

Essays Supporting Implementation of the GRC Sequence

REFLECTION on professional learning, instruction, and dispositions toward science teaching and learning is a vital practice. This chapter is a compilation of essays meant to support you as you implement the GRC instructional sequence in your classroom. The essays are divided into three categories: Placing a Premium on Student Engagement, Actively Engaging as a Professional Teacher, and Important Elements of Productive Classrooms.

Category One: Placing a Premium on Student Engagement

Student learning is more than placing learners in an environment with textbooks and microscopes. Teachers are responsible for positioning students at the center of the teaching and learning process and motivating them to become active learners. It is not about the students gaining information, it is about learning how to learn. Student proficiency in three-dimensional performances develops through engagement with the natural world.

Essay A. Investigating Investigations
Essay B. Implications of the Vision Behind the NGSS for Science Teaching and Learning
Essay C. Curiosity and Science Learning
Essay D. A Vignette of Classroom Discourse to Engage Teachers in Professional Learning

Category Two: Actively Engaging as a Professional Teacher

Becoming an effective teacher is an ongoing and continuous process that extends throughout a professional teaching career. As teachers, we have an ethical responsibility to be lifelong learners. Reflecting on our practices expands our repertoire of strategies and enhances understanding of how students learn.

Essay E. Professional Learning in Science
Essay F. The Role of Professional Science Teacher Associations

Category Three: Important Elements of Productive Classrooms

Exemplary teachers, armed with current research and abreast of innovations, are eager to implement new approaches to reach their students. They savor the opportunity of discovering new strategies and maintain enthusiasm and a disposition to nurture learning in children. Professional teachers also exemplify the virtues they seek to impart in their students: a love of learning, risk-taking, open-mindedness, and an appreciation and respect for the culture and human diversity.

Essay G.   Using the *Going 3D with GRC* Website

Essay H.   Literacy for Science

Essay I.   The Importance of Culture and Place in Science Teaching and Learning

We wish to thank our friends for their contributions to the essays. We greatly appreciate and respect the breadth and depth of experience, expertise, and insights they bring to these essays.

Essay A

Investigating Investigations

Kenneth L. Huff

The vision of the *Framework* was to heighten awareness of science educators about the prominent role of scientific investigations and engineering design in student learning. *Science and Engineering for Grades 6-12: Investigation and Design at the Center* (NASEM, 2019) is an affirmation of this prominence, and as such, recommends science investigation and engineering design as the central approach for teaching science and engineering. This report concluded engaging students in learning about natural phenomena and engineering challenges via science investigation and engineering design increases their understanding of how the world works (p. 4). In the past, many teachers lamented that they did not have sufficient time to address all aspects of the curriculum. This led to teachers telling students science facts and requiring memorization of vocabulary terms, and students feeling science was a game of recalling boring, incomprehensible facts.

Science and Engineering in Grades 6-12 advocates for an instructional approach in which teachers eschew comprehensive overviews of science subjects, and instead engage students in a series of in-depth investigations. The research recommends abandoning the one-size-fits-all textbooks in favor of student engagement through investigations that contextualize real-world phenomena in the science classroom. The teachers' role in the classroom becomes transformed into one of a facilitator of student reasoning as students plan and carry out investigations. Scientific reasoning is intimately intertwined with conceptual knowledge of phenomena being investigated.

Improving student learning in science requires modifying our pedagogical approach with a new emphasis on student reasoning about the causes of phenomena and using evidence to support this reasoning. Harnessing the power of investigation in a science classroom can occur in several ways: 1) engage students in three-dimensional performances in which they make sense of phenomena; 2) develop student-centered, relevant investigations that cultivate interest about science phenomena; and 3) foster social interaction that supports cognitive processes and pushes student thinking toward increasingly sophisticated levels. A key role of the teacher, therefore, is to structure performances during which students build upon prior knowledge and develop evidence-based explanations for the causes of phenomena.

> *The teachers' role in the classroom becomes transformed into one of a facilitator of student reasoning as students plan and carry out investigations.*

Investigations are systematic. They require clarification of what counts as data, identification of necessary tools for data collection, and identification of variables or constraints during the planning process. Students' goal for an investigation is to gather data and information that can be used as evidence to support explanations for the causes of phenomena. Students should carefully and systematically organize and analyze the data to determine its consistency with the accepted explanations for the phenomena and interrogate any inconsistencies. In essence, the struggle in carrying out science investigations is determining the value of the data and information as evidence that supports an explanation.

Teaching moments are created when students connect data to explanations. We want students to reason with a purpose and have a purpose for reasoning. This means when students collect data and/or information they understand why they are gathering it. This provides the opportunity and motivation for meaningful conversations that promote productive classroom discourse about the meaning of the data. For example, the teacher may prompt students with questions such as "How is this pattern different after more energy is added to the system?" "How does changing one component in a system affect the stability of the system?" and "Are there outliers in the data and if so, how should they be addressed?" When students think about these questions, this in-depth reasoning helps them see that science is a social enterprise as they engage in discourse and critique in dialogue with their peers.

Student ideas and concepts in science are generative and build over time. Engaging students in a series of structured learning episodes focused on applying ideas and concepts to a series of analogous phenomena builds students' ability to make sense of novel phenomena they encounter beyond the classroom. Science classes centered on investigation provide multiple opportunities for students to learn science by doing science. Investigations provide students with operational knowledge of the nature of how science works.

Reference

National Academies of Sciences, Engineering, and Medicine. (2019). *Science and engineering for grades 6-12: Investigation and design at the center.* Washington, DC: The National Academies Press.

Implications of the Vision Behind the NGSS for Science Teaching and Learning

Wil van der Veen

The *NGSS* are much more than a set of standards. They represent an innovative way of thinking about science teaching and learning based on the vision described in *A Framework for K-12 Science Education* (NRC, 2012). Central to this vision is that science learning in grades K-12 should be more than learning or memorizing a set of theoretical ideas (e.g., Newton's Laws, atomic structure, natural selection) or processes (e. g. , photosynthesis, mitosis, water cycle). Science education should be more than an endless set of "hands-on" activities or games to demonstrate, prove, or confirm the ideas that scientists have discovered. We do not need to spend days or weeks proving to students that the world consists of particles that are too small to see, or that the acceleration of an object depends on the ratio of force acting on the object and its mass. It may help us better remember these ideas, but it does not teach us how we can use these ideas to make sense of the world we live in.

The key to implementing the *NGSS* is an understanding of the role of natural phenomena in science teaching and learning. Natural phenomena are observable events that can be explained and/or predicted using our knowledge of science. Natural phenomena provide students with opportunities to use core ideas, crosscutting concepts, and engage in using the practices to construct explanations and support them with arguments for how and why the evidence supports the explanation. Once students construct an explanation for a particular phenomenon, they can now also make sense of a host of analogous phenomena. If a student can explain why a rock feels cold on a winter day, they can also explain why the same rock feels warm on a hot summer day or why ice tea left on the counter warms up and hot tea left on the counter cools off.

> *If we support students in constructing explanations for natural phenomena, we provide them with the tools to make sense of a variety of phenomena for the rest of their lives.*

These phenomena are not simply a hook to get students' attention; rather, they drive the instruction from start to finish. Students use crosscutting concepts to guide their thinking about the phenomena, they use practices to engage with and reason about the phenomena, and they apply their understanding of core ideas and other phenomenon-specific information to construct an explanation for the phenomena. Most resources that claim to be *NGSS* aligned are not well aligned. These resources are focused on telling (i.e., demonstrate, prove, confirm) about the science ideas, concepts, and processes, but do not provide opportunities for students to use these ideas, concepts, and processes to construct explanations for phenomena. If phenomena are present in these materials, they are mostly used as a hook and an excuse to teach science ideas or processes. The goal of many materials, not aligned to *NGSS*, is to teach the ideas and processes instead of using these ideas and processes to construct explanations for the causes of phenomena. As a result, science ideas and processes remain largely disconnected from students' observations of the world.

So why is this shift so challenging? The science education we have all experienced and the way we have been teaching science for decades has been focused on teaching science ideas disconnected from the world students experience outside the classroom. After 13+ years of science education, adults find it challenging to link the science they have learned to observable events they encounter in their daily lives. We see over and over again that science teachers find it challenging to connect the science ideas they know and teach every day to natural phenomena beyond their classroom. We have heard high school physics teachers tell us that physics in *NGSS* is difficult because there are no phenomena in physics. We have seen high school biology teachers struggle to identify natural phenomena related to cells or cell processes, or high school chemistry teachers who struggle to connect the periodic table to natural phenomena.

> *Cultivating student wondering requires teachers to respond to student questions in ways that extend thinking rather than provide answers.*

I have struggled as well to connect core ideas to natural phenomena, and have thought about what helped me make these connections. I realized that it was not enough to observe or take pictures of natural phenomena around us — we have to practice and connect phenomena to core ideas as soon as we observe them. If we see a squirrel gather food for winter, we may think about the relationship to the basic needs of living things and that there is something about the structure of the squirrel that helps it to function this way. As I began making connections between phenomena I observed and the core ideas that underlie the phenomena, I created a mental database that I could use to do the reverse. For example, if I need to teach about the structure and function of living things or about the basic needs of animals, I now think of a squirrel gathering food.

If we support students in constructing explanations for natural phenomena, we provide them with the tools to make sense of a variety of related phenomena for the rest of their lives. They will be able to explain why it is hot in the attic and cool in the basement during the summer months, or why it is harder to start and stop a full cart full of groceries as compared to an empty cart. They will be able to explain why adding fish may change a pond, or how removing trees and plants near a river may change the river banks. Using phenomena to initiate science instruction will help make science more relevant for our students, both in and outside the classroom.

Reference
National Research Council. (2012). *A framework for k-12 science education: Practices, crosscutting concepts, and core ideas.* Washington, DC: The National Academies Press.

Essay C

Curiosity and Science Learning

Brett D. Moulding

Curiosity is a natural human emotion that motivates students to investigate the causes of phenomena. We are all curious about the natural and engineered world in which we live. The greater a child's exposure to the natural world, the more often they will wonder about the causes of the phenomena they encounter. The questions students ask are a good indicator of their wondering. Questions provide students with a passport to focus their wondering and extend students' curiosity about the world in which they live. We should encourage students to ask questions, write their questions in a journal, and reflect on them over time.

Cultivating student wondering requires teachers to respond to student questions in ways that extend thinking rather than provide answers. Recently on a hike with my five-year-old granddaughter Lily, I was confronted with a reminder of the complexity of young children's thinking and how questions are an invitation to wonder. We were hiking the trail around String Lake in Teton National Park when she said "Why are these mountains different than the ones at home?" Lily lives in Tucson, Arizona. Well, as you may know, grandfathers are expected to know everything, so I was tempted to tell her "Well Lily, the mountains in Tucson are made of sedimentary rock and the ones here are exposed igneous basement rock." Fortunately, I have been a teacher much longer than a grandfather and paused to respond as a teacher, "Lily, that is a very good question, what is it about these mountains that seem different to you?" Lily immediately responded, "The trees are different!" Lily was wondering about things that I had not even thought about. The predominant trees in the mountains near Tucson, Arizona are Saguaro Cactus and in Teton predominant trees are lodgepole pine. Lily had observed a phenomenon and we talked and wondered about trees for the next 20 minutes. The conversation was even longer the next day. Children's questions are an invitation to wonder about a world they are seeing for the first time. A child's world is wonder-filled. Our responsibility as teachers is to extend the wondering and support their sense-making around phenomena.

Teachers rely on a cadre of skills, tools, and dispositions to extend student thinking. One of the most important skills is the ability to listen and value student questions. Student questions improve when we value them in our classroom. One of the tools is a set of teacher questions that help students "develop questions." Asking questions is different than developing questions. When students first encounter a phenomenon, they may ask preliminary questions. The teacher's role is to extend student thinking by prompting them to develop questions that guide investigations. A strategy teachers use is to have some standard questions to initiate observation of phenomena. Questions such as "What did you observe? What questions can help us investigate this phenomenon? What patterns did you observe? How would changing affect _____? What things are changing in this system?" When teachers use questions to extend thinking they fuel students wondering. Teachers' questions include crosscutting concepts to focus student attention on specific aspects of the phenomenon. Additionally, prompting through questions models the type of questions we hope students will pose as they investigate phenomena beyond the classroom.

> *Our responsibility as teachers is to motivate students to learn.*

Science and Engineering for Grades 6 - 12 (NASEM, 2019) provide two relevant conclusions addressing curiosity:

- Teachers can use students' curiosity to motivate learning by choosing phenomena and design challenges that are interesting and engaging to students, including those that are locally and/or culturally relevant (p. 4).
- Science investigation and engineering design give middle and high school students opportunities to engage in the wider world in new ways by providing agency for them to develop questions and establish the direction for their own learning experiences (p. 4).

Relevant and interesting phenomena can pique students' curiosity and lead to greater interest and identity in science. Our responsibility as teachers is to motivate students to learn.

The best teachers are curious about the natural and designed world. They bring interesting ideas and objects into the classroom and model their own genuine curiosity with students. Teachers who consistently model positive dispositions toward science and model lifelong learning help students to become more curious. Some teachers even pursue their own science investigations in full view of the students and have ongoing experiments in their classrooms. These classrooms are filled with interesting gadgets, ant farms, aquariums, plants, and other items that foster curiosity. Modeling the dispositions of science is an important part of teaching science.

Curiosity helps us enjoy the world in which we live. Every day of our lives should be spent wondering about the phenomena surrounding us. Most of our questions only lead to more questions, but that is an important part of wondering. On any typical day, we should encounter five to ten phenomena to think about, and children may encounter ten to twenty phenomena to wonder about.

Investigation and design are a better way to teach science by virtue of better student engagement. Three-dimensional science teaching and learning can help students become more curious; however, instruction must shift to embrace curiosity as an essential aspect of science learning. Lily is entering Kindergarten this year as a very curious five-year-old. I wonder if she will be as curious when she leaves the 12th grade. Perhaps our goal for science education should be that all students are more curious as high school seniors than they were entering Kindergarten.

Reference
National Academies of Sciences, Engineering, and Medicine. (2019). *Science and engineering for grades 6-12: Investigation and design at the center.* Washington, DC: The National Academies Press.

A Vignette of Classroom Discourse to Engage Teachers in Professional Learning

Brett D. Moulding and Kenneth L. Huff

Classroom discourse is a necessary consideration prior to engaging students in science learning. Discourse refers to the communication patterns of a classroom. Rather than the typical initiate, response, evaluate (IRE) sequence between the teacher and one student, a more productive pattern is students communicating ideas with peers and the teacher. A primary objective of open classroom discourse is to provide a forum for all students to share their ideas and consider others' ideas. This engagement with others' ideas results in explanations that are better supported by appropriate evidence or scientific reasoning (NASEM, 2019). Productive discourse has many benefits in the classroom. The NRC (2008) identified various ways in which classroom discourse is important:

> [I]t allows students' prior ideas to surface which in turn helps the teacher assess their understanding, allowing students to talk about their thinking gives them more opportunities to reflect on, participate in, and build scientific thinking, it provides a context in which students can develop more mature scientific reasoning. (p. 92)

The short vignette presented here provides an example of classroom discourse, an exchange of ideas among students, guided by the teacher. Note that the teacher is not the only person who asks and answers questions. The exchange among the students is an indication of productive, respectful discourse. This instruction is in the middle school grade band and related to students developing understanding consistent with *NGSS* MS-PS1-4: *Develop a model that predicts and describes changes in particle motion, temperature, and state of a pure substance when thermal energy is added or removed.* In this example, stability and change are coupled with other crosscutting concepts to investigate a phenomenon – in this case, the appearance of water droplets on the outside of a glass of ice water. These three days of instruction are part of a larger investigation on the structure of matter.

This essay is intended to serve as an opportunity for professional reflection on ways to use crosscutting concepts to prompt student reasoning. You may wish to use this essay for a PLC with other teachers or for personal reflections on teaching and learning.

Using Crosscutting Concepts to Engage Students in Classroom Discourse

Day One - Instruction begins when students carefully observe a large glass of ice water the teacher has placed before each pair of students.

Teacher: Explore the phenomena you observe with the glass of ice water on your table. Write your observations in your notebooks.

After several minutes of students observing and writing, the teacher poses the question, *"What phenomena did you observe?"* As students contribute to the discussion, the teacher writes a list of student observations of the phenomena on the board.

Lalani: The glass is cold.

Joseph: The outside of the glass is wet.

Cali: Water is rolling off the glass and onto the table.

Miguel: The ice seems to be melting.

Teacher: These observations seem to be about things that are changing. What are some good questions to ask in order to investigate the causes of change in the glass of ice water and the surrounding systems? With your partner, please develop questions to help us investigate the causes of change in the systems.

Students work in pairs to develop questions. Most questions are about matter and energy and the causes of changes that result in water moving from one system to another system. Typical student questions include *"What changed? Where did the water on the glass come from? How does energy change the water? How does water change? Why is water stable?"*

The teacher writes the students' questions on the board. The class discusses the questions and decides to investigate the question *What changes led to water appearing on the outside of the glass?*

The teacher prompts students with the following sequence of performances (science practices are shown in blue, crosscutting concepts in green):

1. Plan and carry out an investigation to generate evidence of the changes in matter and energy that caused water to appear on the outside of the glass.

    (possible materials: paper, string, plastic sandwich bags, access to a freezer-faculty room, 2 small glass jars from the freezer, 2 glass jars left at room temperature, pencil, rubber band, balloons, straw, ice cubes, water, and other materials upon request)

The teacher shows the next slide to prompt students to develop a model:

2. Develop a model to show the changes in matter and energy between systems of the air and the glass that cause water droplets to appear on the glass.

    Having students develop a model prior to classroom discourse is a productive strategy. Students are better prepared to contribute to classroom discourse when provided time to develop a model prior to discussion. This strategy also fosters a safe learning environment for students.

3. Construct an explanation supported by evidence for how changes in energy between the systems of the glass jar and system of the air are causing matter (water) to move from the air to the glass.

Student investigations include breathing on the glass jar; putting empty glass jars in the freezer to get them cold and then taking them out and observing; putting glass jars in plastic bags and placing them into the freezer, then taking them out and observing changes on the glasses in bags compared to a glasses not in a bag. Some students observe changes to glasses containing water at different temperatures. Other students use variations of these types of investigations.

Day Two - The Teacher engages students in a class discussion.

Teacher: So, did the glass of ice water as a system ever become stable?

Maria: Yeah, the next day the ice all melted and the water on the outside of the glass dried up.

Lalani: We didn't see what happened when the ice all melted, but Maria said that it would stop changing when the ice was all melted.

James: I agree with Maria because I have seen this before at home.

Teacher: What caused the ice water system and the air system to change?

Kaapo: Water came out of the air.

Donna: Water in the air is a gas. There is a transfer of energy from the air to the cold glass.

Cali: Water moved from one system to another system. Energy changes it.

Teacher: How did the energy change it?

Cali: You know, the energy changed so the water changed.

Teacher: Let me see if I understand what you are saying. Are you saying that when matter changes, energy is involved? In this case, when the water molecules in the air collide with the cold glass, the energy moves from the gas water molecules into the ice and water in the glass. When enough energy has left the gas molecules, they become liquid water on the outside of the glass. Is that right?

Cali: Yeah, that is what we are saying. Energy goes from one system to another and matter goes from the air to the glass.

James: Cali, what do you mean by matter goes from the air to glass?

Cali: The liquid water on the glass came from the water vapor in the air.

James: Oh, yeah there's water in the air.

Teacher: What evidence do you have to support that explanation? Talk to your partners and write your evidence in your notebook.

After several minutes the teacher asks: *So, what evidence do you have that energy is going from the water in the air to the glass?*

Lalani: In our investigation, we used empty glasses from the freezer and frost formed on them when we took them out, but not on the glass we had inside of the baggie. So we think this means the water is coming from the air. Air could not get inside the bag, so it stayed dry.

Teacher:	This is good, you have evidence of where the matter is coming from, but does anyone have evidence that the change is due to the transfer of energy?
James:	Well, you know when we let the glass sit on the table for a long time, the ice melted and you know it takes heat to melt the ice so energy is moving from the air to melt the ice. The ice would not change if you didn't put energy into the glass.
Kaapo:	Yeah, it takes energy to cause water to evaporate, so just like James said, it must give the energy back when it condenses on the glass.
Teacher:	What do you mean by evaporating and condensing?
Lalani:	In fourth grade, we learned when water changes from a liquid to a gas it evaporates and when it changes from a gas to a liquid it condenses.
Teacher:	Do we all know how this happens? Perhaps we can draw a model to help us understand how energy is involved when matter changes from a liquid to a gas and from a gas to a liquid. Let's begin the model by showing where in the system water evaporates and where it condenses. So, now square your pair to have four in each group and use one of the big sheets of butcher paper to revise your model for the changes in the system. Be sure to define your system in the model and describe the changes to matter and energy in your model.

The teacher shows the next slide to prompt students to develop a model:

4. Revise your model to show the changes in matter and energy between systems of the air and the glass that cause water droplets to appear on the glass.

When students revise their models following the class discussion, it provides opportunities for students to incorporate new ideas they have learned from the discussion. This is an effective way to support students revising their thinking in light of new evidence.

Day Three - The lesson continues with discussion and presentations of student models. The teacher continues to prompt students with couplets of crosscutting concepts, which helps students to become increasingly proficient at using stability and change to describe the causes of the phenomenon. The teacher continues to focus students on changes in matter and energy that cause the phenomenon.

The teacher's first question to students during this investigation was about the causes of changes in the systems. Defining the boundaries of systems helped students describe changes between the systems of 1) the glass of ice water, and 2) the atmosphere. When students first defined the systems, they were better able to use the crosscutting concept of stability and change as a lens to describe the interactions between the two systems. This led them to think about the causes of the changes among systems. Students' initial observations of the glass affirmed that the system was not stable over short periods of time.

As students worked to develop questions, the teacher was able to listen and gather insights into student reasoning about energy and matter. Their learning quickly shifted to new questions about patterns in the qualitative data. This changed the focus of the discussion on how inputs, outputs, and flow of energy between the glass of ice water and the surrounding system caused the phenomenon. Reasoning about the ways energy changes matter provided students with a conceptual understanding of how systems operate.

The couplet of crosscutting concepts among systems, matter and energy, and stability and change in this investigation is useful for helping students to making sense of this phenomenon. Students use the idea that matter does not change unless energy is absorbed or released. Students' understading of system stability focuses on inputs, outputs, and flow of energy within and among systems.

Effective science teaching and learning includes communication and collaboration that require both spoken and written representations of the world (NRC, 2008). Classroom discourse is most effective when teachers actively listen to students describing their understanding and help them strengthen their ideas. Students incorporate the ideas, observations, and investigations into their existing understanding of how the world operates. Classroom discourse is a powerful way to support students in constructing new knowledge.

Using this Essay for Professional Learning

One possible use of this essay is to initiate a professional learning community (PLC) to engage teachers in discussions about ways to conduct purposeful classroom discourse. If you have the opportunity to participate in PLCs, consider using this essay as a tool to help you better understand the importance of classroom discourse. This essay can help teachers understand the importance of 1) extending student thinking and building on classmates ideas, 2) creating an environment for making students thinking visible as they explain their science reasoning and use of ideas and concepts, and 3) helping all students develop a shared and accurate understanding of the core ideas and concepts that support explanations for the causes of phenomena.

PLCs, like all professional learning experiences, are predicated on teachers considering research-based approaches to science instruction. The more closely these experiences are aligned to classroom teaching and learning, the more impactful these experiences are for improving instruction. During professional development, teachers should have opportunities to reflect and discuss with colleagues' instructional decisions and insights about teaching and learning experiences (NASEM, 2019). These collegial discussions help teachers develop a value for specific structures and strategies for instruction in their own classrooms. The most important professional learning occurs when teachers apply it to their own instructional practice and reflect on student learning. Reflection is what changes professional development into professional learning.

Conducting a PLC on Productive Classroom Discourse

Pre-Session and Review

1. Ask teachers to read the vignette prior to coming to the PLC.

Round Robin - 15 minutes

Start the PLC by engaging teachers in a round-robin on the following questions.

3. What are some advantages of engaging students in classroom discourse?

4. How do you use discourse in your own classroom?

Shift to an interactive discussion using the following questions - 30 minutes

5. How did the teacher use crosscutting concepts to focus students thinking on specific aspects of the phenomenon?

6. Which core ideas did the students use to respond to the teacher's questions?

7. How does the teacher assess student learning?

8. How did students developing a model contribute to the classroom discussion?

Reflection and Closure - Write Reflections in Teaching Journal

9. How do classroom environment and culture affect the discussion in your classroom?

10. How did the sequence of practices help the teacher move students from gather to reason, to communicate reasoning?

Professional learning takes place when teachers invest the time and energy to engage in dialogue with colleagues that results in greater understanding of teaching and learning. The outcome of this investment can be measured by changes in instruction and student acquisition of the science knowledge and skills essential for future success beyond the classroom. Professional development is most effective when it is collaborative, focused on student learning, and models a positive classroom culture. When PLCs meet these criteria, they can serve as one element of effective professional development that advances teacher professional learning.

References

National Academies of Sciences, Engineering, and Medicine. (2019). *Science and engineering for grades 6-12: Investigation and design at the center.* Washington, DC: The National Academies Press.

National Research Council. (2008). *Ready, set, science! Putting research to work in K-8 science classrooms.* Washington, DC: The National Academies Press.

Professional Learning in Science

Tiffany Neill and Brett D. Moulding

Teachers are professionals and throughout their careers continue to grow and learn. As professionals, teachers engage in professional learning enabling them to make research-informed decisions about how students learn. Teachers, as professional educators, strive to know how best to teach their students.

Professional learning begins with undergraduate or graduate teacher preparation programs and continues throughout an educator's career. Professional development that contributes the most to instructional changes has four specific attributes that make these experiences effective at improving teaching and learning consistent with the vision presented in *A Framework for K-12 Science Education*. Effective professional development 1) engages teachers in three-dimensional science performances that model the instruction we hope to see in the classroom; 2) provides teachers with resources and strategies to apply these models to classroom instruction; 3) is coherent and sustained in duration and learning experiences, and 4) respects teachers as professionals and teaching as a profession (Council of State Science Supervisors, 2018). Research demonstrates that professional learning experiences that are sustained, coherent, and connected to the classroom work of teachers are more effective at making instructional changes (NASEM, 2015).

Effective professional development models instruction we hope teachers will use to engage students in three-dimensional science performances because modeling classroom instruction is effective at supporting instructional change (NASEM, 2019). High quality professional learning experiences are critical for preparing teachers to engage students in scientific investigation and classroom discourse. Teachers who have not themselves utilized the three-dimensions to make sense of scientific phenomena will struggle to engage students in a scientific investigation. Teachers need professional development opportunities in which they engage in scientific investigation and reflect on how the structure of the instruction provided them with the knowledge to use science and engineering practices to obtain evidence needed to construct explanations. The core ideas and crosscutting concepts are used to support these explanations. Professional development should engage teachers with the same emotions, curiosity, and fascination we hope to use to motivate our students and model dispositions toward curiosity that motivates learning.

Professional development that models three-dimensional performances provides educators with insight into how to enagage their own students. When teachers engage in three-dimensional performances, they not only see how instruction progresses but gain insights into how their students feel when engaged in making sense of phenomena. This emotional component is important in multiple ways. First, it helps teachers understand the importance of curiosity in motivating themselves as well as students. Second, the teacher feels the sense of wonder and joy that comes from seeing phenomena in the world around them. Third, teachers acquire a sense of accomplishment when they apply the learning to make sense of other phenomena in their world. Additionally, modeling helps teachers become sensitive to the nuances of instruction that are too often overlooked (e.g., a pause by the instructor to allow time to think, the arc of development of good questions, talk moves to extend thinking). Professional development that models teaching and learning is one of the most effective ways for teachers to envision instructional change. Most importantly modeling instruction creates powerful opportunities for reflection and discussion.

Effective professional development provides teachers with resources and strategies to apply learning to their own classroom instruction. Teachers do not truly buy into instructional changes until they make them their own. When participating in professional development experiences, teachers need to have the resources to apply the intended changes to their own students. This requires teachers to use grade-level specific lessons, consistent with the professional development, in their own classroom. Professional development leads to professional learning when teachers apply instructional changes in the classroom.

The resources provided for teachers should be accessible, flexible, and engaging for students. Teachers should be provided with strategies to adapt the resources to make them relevant for their students' culture and place. The phenomena in the resources should be fun and engaging and pique student curiosity and interest. The investigations and lessons used in professional development should be consistent with the grade-level and contain scaffolds to support teacher and student learning. These resources should include formative assessment of students' ability to engage in three-dimensional performances (NASEM, 2019).

> *High quality professional learning experiences are critical for preparing teachers to engage students in scientific investigation and classroom discourse.*

Effective professional development is coherent and sustained in duration and learning experience. Coherent learning experiences use consistent and relevant instructional strategies. These experiences provide teachers with clear and consistent ways to engage students in three-dimensional performances. The duration of professional development should create sufficient iterations so that teachers can learn, apply the professional development in their classroom, reflect on effectiveness, and return to additional professional learning experiences that sustain instructional improvement. Teachers value the instructional strategies that are effective in improving student learning. Sustained professional development of sufficient duration is associated with changes to educators' science instruction and provides teachers with time to implement new instructional strategies and reflect on the effectiveness of new approaches to teaching and learning (NASEM, 2015).

Professional development is more effective when teachers are respected as professional educators. Teaching is a profession and teachers should be respected throughout professional development sessions. Teachers should have opportunities to be heard and their concerns and ideas considered. High-quality professional development provides opportunities for discussion and respects teachers' ideas while creating time for reflection on these ideas. Teachers' time should be honored with sessions starting and end-ing at the designated times. Presenters should be well qualified and know how to utilize the expertise of the teachers participating in the sessions. Teachers should have opportunities to communicate via email and social media with presenters following sessions and receive appropriate and timely responses to their emails.

Professional teachers participate in professional development and, throughout their career, improve the skills, knowledge, and dispositions to be a high-quality teacher. Professional teachers are continually improving their skills and maintain an open mind about new ideas and strategies for teaching. Continual improvement and reflection on teaching and learning is one of the hallmarks of a professional teacher.

Professional teachers engage in professional learning opportunities that extend past the professional development event. Teachers apply the learning from professional development to their classroom, reflect on the instructional strategies presented, and critically analyze how professional learning can be used to improve student learning. Reflection about our professional growth and our students' learning becomes a daily and welcomed routine.

The Council of State Science Supervisors (CSSS), a professional association made up of science educators from each state, has developed the *Science Professional Learning Standards* (SPLS). These standards describe the attributes of quality professional development and inform both the provider and participants about the expectations of quality professional learning experiences. We encourage you to review these standards as you design professional development or select professional learning opportunities.

Each day, teachers make a difference in the lives of students. Teaching science goes far beyond the science content and affects students' disposition and identity with science. The way we teach science also affects our identity as teachers of science. Teaching science is rewarding and enjoyable. We should cherish our profession and know that the harder we work, the greater our self-satisfaction and the more we will enjoy teaching.

References

Council of State Science Supervisors. (2018). *Science professional learning standards.* Available at http://cosss.org/Professional-Learning

National Academies of Sciences, Engineering, and Medicine. (2015). *Science teachers' learning: Enhancing opportunities, creating supportive contexts.* Washington, DC: The National Academies Press.

National Academies of Sciences, Engineering, and Medicine. (2019). *Science and engineering for grades 6-12: Investigation and design at the center.* Washington, DC: The National Academies Press.

TIFFANY NEILL serves as Executive Director of Curriculum and Instruction, Oklahoma State Department of Education. Tiffany is the Co-Principal Investigator for the National Science Foundation Project, ACESSE, working directly with thirteen states to promote equity and coherence in state science education systems. She is a past President of the Council of State Science Supervisors.

Essay F

The Role of Professional Science Teacher Associations

Renae Pullen and Kenneth L. Huff

National associations of science education (e.g., National Science Teaching Association, National Science Education Leadership Association) share similar goals and missions: to champion science literacy, promote excellence in science teaching and learning, and advocate for high-quality science education. Science teacher associations have and continue to take an active role in initiating transformation in science teaching and learning. The goals of national associations are often reflected in the mission and goals of association state chapters (e.g., Science Teachers Association of New York State, Utah Science Teachers Association). Successful state associations look to the future and possess a compelling vision and strategic plan for high-quality science education. This vision and plan empowers its members to find their role in the association, enables others to feel as though they make a difference, and enhances the profession with research-informed, sustained professional learning opportunities. Members advocate for policies that promote high-quality science education and help build a community of professionals dedicated to advancing science teaching and learning. This includes pre-kindergarten and elementary teachers of science who are members of the association and may be generalists but are deeply committed to improving their science instruction for students; informal science educators; and educators at the university level. Members of state science teachers' associations immerse themselves in the established vision and plan and carry it forward across the state, their districts, and classrooms to make a difference in the science education of students.

A Framework for K-12 Science Education (*Framework*) developed a vision of science education with three distinct, but equally important dimensions of science that are integrated into all levels and disciplines to provide students a coherent conceptual understanding of science. This transformed how teachers approach science instruction in the classroom. Alerting members to what is new and different in three-dimensional standards and phenomena-based instruction is an important role of state science teacher associations. Three-dimensional standards have the potential for a long term and profound impact on science education within individual states, but only if professional associations respond by supporting their members around the changes envisioned by the *Framework*. As this new, innovative vision of science learning and sense-making comes to fruition in science classrooms in the United States, exemplary state professional science teaching associations have led the charge in providing teachers with needed tools, resources, and support. These associations take an active role in initiating transformation in science teaching and learning. Members of professional associations access ideas through networks of like-minded colleagues and build capacity through active engagement. State associations cultivate a community of practice to support teachers as they implement the innovations of three-dimensional science standards.

Providing science educators with sustainable, high-quality professional learning is the hallmark of an outstanding state science teachers' association. State associations build capacity by providing opportunities for members to increase knowledge, skills, and competence through professional development. This often occurs at conferences and meetings that bring teachers of science together to learn about the innovations around three-dimensional standards, implications of phenomena-based learning, and the emerging research that support these changes. Cutting-edge learning sessions presented at conferences elevate the profession and frequently include nationally or internationally renowned practitioners and scholars who speak from their own experience or research. Sessions provided at conferences should reflect contemporary views and hold true to the spirit of the *Framework*. We should eschew sessions that were popular decades ago (e.g., make and take, vocabulary bingo) and instead seek sessions that engage professionals with evidence-based models for instruction in science. State conference sessions should provide teachers with opportunities to learn in the manner they are expected to teach. Mnemonic devices aimed at memorizing the order of planets in the solar system or steps in the scientific method miss the mark and are not consistent with contemporary research on how students learn science. Therefore, these types of sessions should give way to approaches that enable teachers to better understand how students develop conceptual understanding by engaging in performances at the intersection of concepts, ideas, and practices.

> *Providing science educators with sustainable, high-quality professional learning experiences is a hallmark of outstanding state science teachers' association.*

State science conferences provide educators opportunities to collaborate with others in reflecting on the structure of science performances in investigations, and network with colleagues from various membership sections throughout the state to determine how to scale up successful approaches. Extended or short courses are often available for science educators to learn in local informal science spaces like museums, zoos, aquariums, and other science centers. Conferences and professional meetings foster an increased sense of community and collegiality providing members an opportunity to build further coalitions.

State science teacher associations that are dedicated to advancing and improving science education know transformation happens by developing and maintaining strategic partnerships with state boards of education, local districts, and other policymakers. The associations collaborate with boards of education to leverage the wisdom of the classroom teacher and expertise of its membership body to identify high-quality curricular resources and develop professional learning opportunities. Moreover, these partnerships can capitalize on the science teachers' voices to advocate for policies that will advance excellence in science education. State associations should work with state and local boards to ensure their members are represented on councils and committees to provide direct input from the field and advise decision-makers on system changes that will improve science teaching and learning. State associations have the capability to use the voice and expertise of its members to be the drivers of change in policies so barriers like inadequate time, resources, and opportunities are removed, and each student is provided equitable access to meaningful science learning experiences.

Outstanding state science associations promote excellence and innovation in science teaching and learning. They offer grants or share grant opportunities with its membership to help teachers secure and utilize funds to enhance classroom learning experiences. They make members aware of fellowships and synergistic opportunities that will help them develop their voice, grow as a leader in science education, and explore learning opportunities to deepen their knowledge and pedagogical practices. The associations recognize the outstanding contributions its members have made in science education through professional recognition and award programs. These programs do not only celebrate excellence in science education, but they also elevate and expose the exemplary work of science educators do to a larger audience.

Improving outcomes for all students requires that science teachers and leaders initiate a transformation in their approaches, and successful state associations are leading that charge. State science associations play a critical role in supporting change in the policies that inform what happens in the classroom and improving the quality of science teaching and learning. The associations build science educators' capacity through a variety of professional learning opportunities and support collaborative professional networks. Every state association is a reflection of its membership. As a collective voice, state science teachers' associations have the potential to be the force that ensures the vision for science education articulated in the *Framework* is realized.

RENAE PULLEN is the K-6 Science Curriculum Instructional Specialist for Caddo Parish Public Schools in Shreveport, Louisiana. Pullen has been an educator in Caddo Parish for over 20 years. She currently serves as a member of the Board on Science Education for the National Academies of Sciences and is a member of the Science, Technology, Engineering and Mathematics Education Advisory Panel for the National Science Foundation.

Essay G

Using the Going 3D with GRC Website

Kenneth L. Huff

The *Next Generation Science Standards* (*NGSS*) were written to perturb the education system and change teaching to be consistent with how students learn. Standards are an opportunity for you to transform the structure of instruction and shift toward more student-centered teaching and learning. Instructional resources should provide a clear and coherent structure for students to apply their science and engineering knowledge beyond the classroom. Resources should also be consistent with the vision of the *Framework* and have investigation and design at the center of science classroom instruction.

Gather, Reason, Communicate Reasoning (GRC) lessons are aligned to contemporary science standards because they incorporate three-dimensional performances as the central focus of what students do in the classroom as they learn science. The emphasis is on using a full suite of practices, bringing select crosscutting concepts to the forefront, and applying students' increased understanding of core ideas to construct explanations of phenomena.

When the practices, concepts, and ideas work together as a tapestry they provide coherence in instruction. Coherence can be viewed as the relationship or connectedness of one performance to the next so there is a conceptual flow of ideas. This leads to a more sophisticated understanding of core ideas and crosscutting concepts. GRC lessons provide coherence because they use a consistent structure based upon the *Framework* where students use the three dimensions to make sense of phenomena across lessons, grades, and science disciplines.

The lessons on *Going3DwithGRC* website are coherent and aligned to the *NGSS* and contemporary three-dimensional science standards. The website resources provide teachers with a set of tools to structure instruction that is consistent with research on how students learn science. The traditional paradigm of using textbooks to present the central parts of disciplinary core ideas, and having students then explain them back does not reflect contemporary research or three-dimensional nature of lessons used throughout most states. GRC lessons are different from traditional approaches because they are about creating opportunities for students to reason.

Lesa Rohrer, Brett Moulding, and Kenneth Huff work with teachers to maintain the website that contains all the necessary resources needed to help you to build your own GRC lessons. Lesson ideas on the website provide teachers of science with examples of how to engage students in science performances at the intersection of the three dimensions. These lesson ideas should be viewed as starting points from which instruction is adapted and responsive based on the specific needs of the students in your classroom.

Perhaps the most meaningful resource on the website is the over 300 vetted, free, three-dimensional elementary, middle, and high school lessons. If seeking a GRC lesson at the K-5 level, click on Elementary

Lessons and this will take you to GRC lessons in this grade band. Click on a grade and a matrix populated with GRC lessons by standard and further categorized by discipline (life, physical, Earth and space science) will appear. The link opens the lesson as a Google document.

At the middle and high school levels, lessons are categorized by disciplinary core ideas. The matrix at each grade band provides information about the state where teachers who developed the lesson reside and the lesson topic from the *Framework* and *NGSS*. You will find that most *NGSS* standards have a lesson across the K-12 spectrum and many standards have multiple GRC lessons to use and reflect upon. A few of the lessons are labeled as "under construction" for various reasons including the absence of a student reading in the gathering component, or incomplete formative assessment for student learning. We encourage you to share with us recommendations for modifications to the GRC lessons you use in your classroom. We continue to work with teachers across the country to develop new lessons and make daily enhancements to lessons and website resources to ensure it is most useful for teachers.

The website resources are provided to support you in helping your students as they build on their prior understandings, incrementally extending and revising these understandings as they use practices in meaningful ways to explore phenomena. Our purpose is to provide users with tools to structure instruction so students learn how to learn, not for teachers to be conveyors of information. It is certainly easier to ask students questions rather than having them develop their own questions, and it is easier to tell students information rather than having them gather it on their own. The lessons on the website were developed by teachers and have been used in their classrooms. The lessons feature embedded formative assessment, teaching suggestions, and instructions for obtaining the necessary materials to teach the lesson in your classroom.

The resources on the website support teachers in moving from more traditional pedagogy to research-based approaches to teaching and learning. We trust you will find the website resources to be straightforward and useful for engaging students with science phenomena consistent with the vision of the *Framework*.

Essay H

Literacy for Science

Candace Penrod and Brett D. Moulding

Reading and writing are essential tools for students to engage in scientific reasoning. Investigating the causes of science phenomena, when well presented, generates genuine curiosity and is an effective way to motivate students to read carefully while gathering information. Engaging students with the phenomena first, presented as an observation or event in which students naturally generate questions, can pique interest and create intrinsic motivation for learning. Writing provides students a way to organize thinking and present their reasoning to others. Writing is motivated by a desire to communicate ideas, make sense of curious things, and communicate reasoning to others. When students formalize their reasoning through writing, they can better reflect on their own thinking.

Science teaching and learning should 1) engage students in using reading to obtain information to use as evidence to support science explanations and develop arguments for how the evidence supports the explanation, and 2) engage students in writing to communicate their reasoning for the causes of phenomena.

Jonathan Osborne, Stanford University, argues that "understanding scientific concepts requires engaging in reading, writing, talking, and drawing, in addition to participating in hands-on experiences" (NRC, 2014, p. 20). Reading from reliable sources scaffolds science learning by providing the ideas and concepts students need in order to reason explanations during science investigation. Students use advanced thinking skills to evaluate information that may be used in providing an explanation for the causes of phenomena.

Communicating reasoning often requires writing. Writing is a tool for recording observations and data, determining relationships, and communicating evidence through explanations and arguments. Sharing one's writing requires a safe classroom culture in which student's thinking is valued and respected. When students are motivated by engaging with interesting phenomena, they are motivated to read and write to support their investigations.

Making sense of science phenomena provides a natural integration for reading and gathering information specific to the phenomena being investigated. The *Framework* accentuates the importance of obtaining and communicating information through various modalities including reading, writing, speaking, and listening, highlighting the importance of literacy to communicate and to exchange information in science (NRC, 2012, pp. 74-76). Furthermore, the importance of literacy in science learning is underscored inherently in the science and engineering practices themselves, as students access information in texts in order to gather evidence to support explanations and reasoning, and then communicate their findings through writing and speaking (Moulding, Bybee, & Paulson, 2015).

Literacy for science enhances the traditional role of reading and writing in science classrooms. The *Framework*'s vision is that students engage in reading to obtain information as a gathering practice that will lead to reasoning and explanation. Reading for science should provide students with the information they need to make sense of phenomena.

Reading to Gather Evidence

Science learning begins by engaging students in phenomena, which causes students to become curious. Curiosity motivates students to gather data from hands-on investigations and then read to obtain more information. Too often we think of doing science as only the hands-on investigation, but students should also investigate and gather evidence through reading. This involves evaluating multiple lines of evidence and interpreting data collected from investigations to support the explanations.

Reading and comprehending information in science is different than reading other types of information in three important ways. First, these materials are information-dense and the writing style tends to put significant information in very condensed forms; this includes multiple ideas in a single sentence. Second, the text tends to use graphs, charts, and pictures to communicate ideas. Huff (2016) asserts many science texts are multimodal, using a mix of words, tables, and mathematics to communicate information. This requires the reader to interpret the information from models as part of the text. Third, science text is composed of reliable findings that can be used to make predictions, as opposed to the narrative storyline or fictional characters found in a literary text (Shanahan, 2017). These differences require guidance from the teacher for how to read and interpret models and science text. Reading a science text is quite different from reading a novel or newspaper. The precise meaning of each word or clause may be important. Therefore, science texts must be read accurately to extract information.

Gathering information by reading about complex scientific ideas, such as the theories specific to natural selection and evolution, the inheritance of traits, or Newton's laws, build students' ability to analyze text and connect it to examples in ways that few students have used. Students with limited reading ability may be reluctant to attempt to read these materials, so it is important to first engage students in an investigation before engaging them in reading about phenomena. The key to engaging students is to use strategies that both scaffold the reading and develop high levels of interest.

Strategies for developing text comprehension for early readers include the instructional strategy of a teacher reading a more complex text to the class and then providing the students with a grade-level appropriate text consistent with the teacher reading. Some teachers use this strategy as a way to engage parents in reading with their students and then have students read to parents. This strategy is used in a number of early grade-level GRC lessons available at the *Going3DwithGRC* website. Specific examples include the following lessons: Do You Want to Go to the Beach? K-ESS3-2; Good Vibrations 1-PS4-1; and Un-be-weave-able 2-PS1-3. Teachers should always engage students with the text prior to assigning reading. When reading is integral to hands-on experiences, both the reading and experience become more meaningful. The list below provides a few strategies that have been successful in the classroom.

Pre-Reading – Determine the purpose for reading
1. Engage students with the same phenomenon that is presented in the text. The engagement may

include a hands-on investigation or design and/or observing the phenomenon in pictures or videos.

2. Communicate that students will be gathering evidence from the reading, and provide students with a "reading outline" or anticipation guide.

3. Discuss the structure of the informational text (e.g., headings, graphs, charts, pictures, summary paragraph message). Note: many students are familiar with narrative text structure (story with a plot), but are unaware that informational text does not follow this pattern.

4. Engage students in a discussion of the phenomenon the author is describing and have students identify analogous phenomena from their own experiences.

Gathering – Organize information from the text

5. Prompt students to use key crosscutting concepts to make sense of the text by identifying 1) cause and effect relationships; 2) the system the text is describing (e.g., changes, matter and energy in the system, scale); and, 3) patterns about the phenomena the text describes.

6. Use strategies to have students develop questions they hope to answer from the reading and record the questions in a student notebook or a class chart leaving room for evidence to support an explanation.

7. Prepare a graphic organizer that mimics the structure/content of the text (e.g., an empty pyramid when gathering information about trophic levels, a Venn-diagram when gathering information about friction and gravity).

Reasoning – Evaluate the information presented in the text

8. Students determine and record the author's explanations and relate each to the observed phenomenon.

9. Students determine if the author's argument is supported by both the author's evidence and evidence generated in the student's own investigation. Students use a T-Chart to record each argument and corresponding supporting evidence.

10. After recording multiple lines of evidence in a notebook, circle the pieces that best support the explanation. Then, write a statement above each circle that explains the reasoning as to why this piece of evidence helps support your argument.

Reading is not the only practice students use for gathering evidence. Information can also be gathered through listening to others present information as evidence. The classroom environment where productive listening occurs should be structured carefully to allow for productive discourse and for students to convey what they do and do not understand. Productive and safe learning environments for speaking and listening do not just happen; they are fostered through clear expectations and explicit modeling by the teacher.

Using Literacy to Reveal Student Thinking

Writing is a tool that reveals a student's thoughts and explanations. Whether their writing is a drawing, model, or text, students use writing as a means of making thought visible. Just as students must gather and present evidence to support an explanation, teachers must analyze the evidence students communicate to assess student understanding in explaining phenomena. Thus, it is imperative to capture and reveal students' thinking by making it visible through writing and drawing. Some students are reluctant to commit their reasoning to paper, but when they do, there is much to be gained. Students should be given specific goals for writing and specific timeframes to complete the task. Writing time should be quiet and respected, and is often referred to as "Silent Sustained Writing. "

Verbal discourse is equally important for helping students make thinking visible. Similar to writing, discussion among students should include evidence to support assertions. Whether in small groups or full class discussions, speaking provides opportunities for students to utilize evidence to support assertions and argue for a specific explanation. Speaking is often the first step to writing; however, when using in-class discussion we recommend that students are given a few minutes prior to the discussion to write an explanation. This creates an opportunity for "think time" and ownership to develop the reasoning students will present.

It is important to note that utilizing classroom discussion in ways that focus on student sense-making of new phenomena requires careful planning to develop a deeper understanding of fewer science concepts (NRC, 2007). Instructional planning is required to formulate phenomenon-specific questions that focus students on the science ideas and concepts central to making sense of the phenomenon. Developing intentional questions that empower student sense-making is more important than revealing the "punch-line" of the student performance. Phenomena and questions should be presented to students in ways that give them time and space to apply core ideas and crosscutting concepts to formulate explanations. This requires teachers to engage students in reading and listening to gather evidence and writing and speaking to communicate how the evidence supports explanations.

Closing Thoughts

Inherent in the *Framework* is the intention that students will not only gain knowledge of the practices, crosscutting concepts, and core ideas of science and engineering, but also "be critical consumers of scientific information related to their everyday lives, and continue to learn about science throughout their lives" (NRC, 2012, p. 9). Reaching the vision of all students engaging productively in science learning, requires consistent support literacy for science in our classrooms. Engaging students in gathering and evaluating information to use as evidence is an important aspect of living in an increasingly complex world.

References
Huff, K. L. (2016). Addressing three common myths about the next generation science standards. *Science and Children, 53*(5), 30-33.

Moulding, B. , Bybee, R. , & Paulsen, N. (2015). *A vision and plan for science teaching and learning: An educator's guide to a framework for k-12 science education, next generation science standards and state standards.* Salt Lake City, Utah:Essential Teaching and Learning.

National Research Council. (2007). *Taking science to school: learning and teaching science in grades k-8.* Washington, DC: The National Academies Press.

National Research Council. (2012). *A framework for k-12 science education: Practices, crosscutting concepts, and core ideas.* Washington, DC: The National Academies Press.

National Research Council. (2014). *Literacy for science: Exploring the intersection of the Next Generation Science Standards and Common Core for ELA standards: A workshop summary.* National Academies Press.

Shanahan, T. (2017). *Disciplinary literacy in science.* University of Illinois at Chicago. Retrieved from https://shanahanonliteracy. com/publications

CANDACE PENROD is Salt Lake City School District senior manager and science supervisor. She works with national and district level science education leaders from across the country to promote the importance of literacy in science learning. She was recently awarded a Vernier Emerging Science Education Leader Scholarship at the National Science Education Leadership Association (NSELA) Summer Leadership Institute 2019.

Essay I

The Importance of Culture and Place in Science Teaching and Learning

Stephanie Kamake'e'āina, and Lesa Rohrer

'A'ohe pau ka 'ike i ka halau ho'okahi (All knowledge is not taught in the same school) i.e., there are many sources of knowledge (Pukui, 1983).

Science is one of many ways of making sense of the world (Brickhouse, Lowery, & Shultz, 2000). Science learning is a cultural process rooted in our natural curiosity. Cultivating that curiosity to influence science learning hinges on understanding the role culture and place play in our classrooms. In its broadest sense, culture is the learned behavior of a group of people that generally reflects the tradition of that people and is socially transmitted from generation to generation through social learning; it is also shaped to fit circumstances and goals (NASEM, 2018). Culture is not only a matter of what people learn but also a matter of how they learn.

Learning is influenced by the context in which it takes place. Learning happens as we move in and across the practices of everyday life (including home, school, and neighborhood) to navigate new situations and problems. Science classrooms should embody an environment that makes meaningful connections with the cultural knowledge, experiences, values, and sense-making practices of our students and their communities. Sense-making practices include both the mental and social efforts undertaken to construct an individual and a shared understanding of new information. Sense-making is one way to connect what we know with what we are trying to figure out. Connections learners make include connecting new concepts to prior knowledge and experiences, forming episodic connections to their lived experiences and stories they hear, seeing analogies and contrasts between distinct concepts, and relating abstractions to concrete objects and experiences either literally or metaphorically. As students use their knowledge, more connections are made among concepts (NASEM, 2019.)

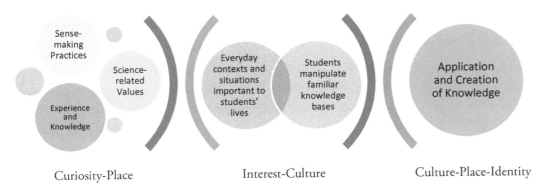

Curiosity-Place   Interest-Culture   Culture-Place-Identity

A community-based context for science learning generates useful language and facilitates communication skills as students apply their learning beyond the classroom. Science learning is enhanced when connections are made to familiar contexts and build on students' prior knowledge (NASEM, 2018). In addition to enhancing student learning, teachers can also nurture curiosity and motivate students by using phenomena related to a community-based context and are relevant to the students in the classroom. To establish relevance there needs to be a connection to learners' interests, such as their communities, cultures, places, experiences, and real-world issues (NASEM, 2019). Science phenomena are observable events that occur in the universe and that we can use scientific knowledge to explain or predict. Phenomena can be the everyday events we see around us, such as a drop of dew glistening on a blade of grass in the morning and then disappearing as the day warms. We encounter hundreds of phenomena in our everyday lives. Phenomena have similar core idea causes and can be connected to culture and place.

An example of a community-based context for science teaching and learning is presented in the following synopsis of a middle school lesson. Stephanie Kamake'e'āina is a middle school teacher at Lokelani School in Maui. She utilizes both culture and place through the gathering, reasoning, and communicating reasoning (GRC) instructional sequence to engage students in sense-making around the core idea of sexual and asexual reproduction found in MS-LS3-2: *Develop and use a model to describe why asexual reproduction results in offspring with identical genetic information and sexual reproduction result in offspring with genetic variation.* The following is a short excerpt of instruction from Stephanie's teaching:

> When science and culture are connected, the students are more engaged in the learning process. In our Life Science class, Standard MS-LS3-2 addresses the idea of Sexual and Asexual Reproduction. There are many different lessons and activities that we could tap into, but we decided that since we lived on an island, why not use something local. There is a world-class aquarium located just a few minutes away from our area and we are two blocks from the beach. Studying reproduction in coral seemed to be a great topic. Most of the students go to the beach and have seen the coral reefs, but did not know how they reproduced. Many did not know that this is a living animal.

> Our lessons started with the phenomenon: "A coral (pūko'a) colony is made of genetically identical individuals." The students were introduced to the Hawaiian word for coral (pūko'a) as well as listening to 'Olelo's about the connection between coral reefs and Hawaiian culture. When they learned that coral (pūko'a) can reproduce sexually and asexually, their interest was piqued. Information about viewing the spawning of coral at our local aquarium was announced in the island newspaper and shared with the students. Watching the spawning in a video is very different from seeing it happening right in front of you. Many of the students were able to view this phenomenon.

You may not have a coral reef where you live, but you most likely have a phenomenon that can be explained with the same core idea. Science teaching and learning framed in local knowledge—in relation to local practices, and land and place-based ways—can enhance the relevance and meaning of the learning. GRC lessons provide a structure for instruction that functions to connect the causes of local phenomena and/or community issues unique to a place through a student-centered approach that supports students in asking questions and finding information that builds sensemaking skills.

Here's how the GRC sequence was used to support context-based learning in the lesson.

Gather	Reason	Communicate
▪ Used local phenomena unique to where the students live. ▪ Connected Hawaiian ōlelo noʻeau that provides traditional explanations of the phenomenon. ▪ Provided opportunities to connect Hawaiʻi specific resources and language.	During the Class Discussion ▪ How and/or why is this phenomenon unique to Hawaiʻi? ▪ How does the explanation of the phenomenon in the moʻolelo connect to the scientific explanation? ▪ How does our history (ancestors and island formation) make the explanation of the phenomenon unique to Hawaiʻi? ▪ How does ōlelo noʻeau help connect our cultural views and values to the explanation of the phenomenon?	Create and sustain a classroom wherein ▪ Students use moʻolelo and/or ōlelo noʻeau in models and explanations. ▪ Students use the Hawaiian language appropriately when speaking or writing. ▪ Students explain their sense-making practices and real-life experiences. ▪ Students develop arguments for how or why the evidence they have collected supports their explanation.

References

Brickhouse, N. W. , Lowery, P. , & Schultz, K. (2000). What kind of a girl does science? The construction of school science identities. *Journal of Research in Science Teaching, 37*(5), 441-458.

National Academies of Sciences, Engineering, and Medicine. (2018). *How people learn II: Learners, contexts, and cultures.* Washington, DC: The National Academies Press.

National Academies of Sciences, Engineering, and Medicine. (2019). *Science and engineering for grades 6-12: Investigation and design at the center.* Washington, DC: The National Academies Press.

Pukai, M. K. (1983). *'Olelo No'eau: Hawaiian proverbs & poetical sayings.* Honolulu, HI: Bishop Museum Press.

STEPHANIE M. KAMAKEʻEʻĀINA is a teacher at Lokelani Intermediate students in Maui, Hawaii. She has spent more than 29 years teaching math and science. Recently, Stephanie has worked with the Hawaii State Department of Education as a member of the Science Content Panel and Work Group to support the implementation of the *NGSS*. During this time, she learned more about the Next Generation Science Standards and Nā Hopena Aʻo so that she could help teachers in Maui learn about the new standards and how to incorporate Hawaiian culture into the lessons. The lesson Stephanie shared can be found at https://tinyurl. com/yyw3fxjj and on the *Going3DwithGRC* lesson website.

LESA L. ROHRER currently serves as the director of data literacy at the state department of education in Oklahoma. Prior to this, she served as the director of curriculum, instruction, and assessment, and secondary science coordinator for Oklahoma City Public Schools. She also served as the career and technical education (CTE) specialist and Indian Education Grant Director for the Northwest Arctic Borough School District in rural Alaska.

Notes

Notes

Chapter 7

Putting It All Together

LEARNING SCIENCE should be fun and enjoyable for both you and your students. An important goal for science education is for students to identify with and enjoy learning science. A positive classroom culture wherein students investigate relevant phenomena helps make science learning enjoyable and memorable, and supports these goals for all students. Curiosity and an understanding of science help make life beyond the classroom rich and interesting. Whether on a nature hike, museum visit, a trip to a national park, or walking in the neighborhood, science learning contributes to the joy of life.

Teaching is a Profession

As a professional, you work every day to improve student learning. This work is informed by your experiences with students, professional development, and research into how students learn. The most important professional learning occurs when you apply your learning from professional development to your own classroom instruction and then reflect on how these changes affect student learning. Reflection is an integral part of professional learning. Teachers make informed decisions about what is best for student learning based on evidence, experience, and current research for best practices.

Professional development is an important way to improve science teaching. Many teachers attend professional development on their own time and expense and rely on these experiences to inspire and inform changes to their teaching. Professional development should be conducted in ways that respect teachers as professionals, model best practices from research, and support teacher learning through authentic engagement with science concepts, skills, and pedagogy. Research-based strategies and structures to create a culture of continuous growth through the application of professional learning is the most effective approach to professional development.

As a professional teacher, you make a difference in the lives of your students both now and in their future. You model curiosity, value for learning, and civil discourse, and contribute to a sense of order critical to lifelong learning. You are an important role model.

Student Learning

When students develop a conceptual understanding of a small set of core ideas and crosscutting concepts, they can apply this understanding to make sense of countless numbers of science phenomena. Proficiency in science is not recalling or reciting ideas and concepts, but rather applying ideas and concepts to make sense of phenomena beyond the classroom. Science learned well lasts a lifetime.

Curiosity is an emotion that motivates student learning and fuels the persistence needed to be successful in science. Curiosity prompts questions and students should be continuously asking questions about the world in which they live. Most of these questions are never shared with anyone but enhance students' desire to learn. Building a safe classroom environment where students are motivated to wonder and ask questions deepens curiosity. Some of the most wonderful student questions are ones never answered, but serve to pique curiosity. Sharing enthusiasm for wondering is contagious and nurtures student curiosity, which leads to interest in science, and interest in science leads to students identifying with science. When students identify with science, they are more likely to pursue science beyond the classroom.

Teachers can create a classroom culture that encourages students to share ideas, ask questions, and construct explanations. Students have the right to present their ideas orally, in writing and with models, and have these ideas considered by classmates and teachers. Students have a responsibility to listen, read, and consider the ideas, models, and writing of others. Effective science classrooms are safe learning environments for all students to share ideas supported by evidence and reasoning and that acknowledge the cultural and linguistic resources students bring to the science classroom (NASEM, 2018).

Science education should help students develop a conceptual structure for understanding useful knowledge for making sense of novel phenomena. The GRC sequence begins with students asking questions. This puts students at the center of learning and honors their curiosity. This instructional sequence is a useful structure to help students develop conceptual understanding. The GRC is consistent with constructivist learning theory, promotes three-dimensional science performances, incorporates meaningful formative assessment, and supports systematic investigation of phenomena beyond the classroom.

Science is a Way of Knowing Based on Empirical Evidence

Science investigations seek evidence to support explanations for the causes of phenomena. Empirical evidence is what distinguishes science from other ways of knowing. Evidence is the hallmark of science and should be an integral part of every science learning experience. Science learning should engage students in making sense of relevant phenomena in the classroom that they apply to make sense of phenomena beyond the classroom. Students are expected to consistently utilize evidence to support science explanations and arguments. An important goal is for students to value and use science as a process of obtaining knowledge based on empirical evidence.

Teaching and Learning Science

Teachers can use science instruction to create a classroom environment and expectations that engage students in science performances — making school science more science-like. This means that students are engaged in science performances to make sense of phenomena that are sometimes novel and sometimes familiar. Science instruction should engage students in seeing previously unnoticed phenomena and leverage student curiosity to motivate learning. Our job as teachers is to motivate students to learn.

Student investigations should be at the center of science instruction. Effective science instruction engages students in gathering information, reasoning with the information to make sense of phenomena, and communicating explanations and arguments for the causes of phenomena. Educational research confirms that deeper engagement in science investigations leads to stronger conceptual understandings of science content than what is demonstrated through more traditional, memorization-intensive approaches. Investigations that engage students in doing science and engineering increase their conceptual knowledge of science and improve their reasoning and problem-solving skills (NASEM, 2019). Investigation and design are more effective in supporting learning than traditional teaching methods.

Three-Dimensional Learning

Standards consistent with the *Framework* are written as three-dimensional student performances. These standards provide a description of student proficiency in science and engineering. Science instruction and lessons that support three-dimensional science learning are more relevant to students than standards but aligned to the same three-dimensions. Lessons should have a series of three-dimensional performances that take students from gathering data and information through investigations to reasoning explanations, and arguments to communicating their reasoning. Along the way, students develop and use models, analyze and interpret data, evaluate information, read, write, and use mathematical and computational thinking.

Science and engineering practices are what students do in science. The practices serve a role much like the cognitive verbs of previous standards. The practices are key to describing students' actions in science performances. The practices are used in GRC lessons to move students from gathering data and information to reasoning explanations and arguments, to communicate their reasoning. The practices are key to learning, but without core ideas and crosscutting concepts, the practices do not empower student learning to go beyond the classroom.

Crosscutting concepts are important tools to help make sense of phenomena across all disciplines of science. Each crosscutting concept is a lens that helps students see different aspects of phenomena. When students use multiple crosscutting concepts in an investigation, they deepen their understanding of the relationships among the components of systems. The crosscutting concepts are also useful tools to use in assessment prompts and during class discussion. The crosscutting concepts can be organized by function into three categories: 1) causality, 2) systems, and 3) patterns. Crosscutting concepts are included in each performance within a GRC lesson and help students to focus on specific aspects of phenomena.

Core ideas describe scientific concepts, laws, and/or parts of theories. Students use core ideas to support explanations of causes of phenomena. Core ideas are not the explanations for phenomena but are used by students to support explanations. Science explains the universe in terms of matter, energy, forces, space, and time. A clear understanding of a small set of core ideas helps students to construct accurate scientific explanations for the causes of phenomena.

GRC lessons provide a structure for engaging students in three-dimensional science performances. The purpose of the GRC lesson sequence is to focus instruction on performances that lead students to reason and communicate that reasoning. The sequence has utility for organizing instruction consistent with the *Framework* and provides a structure for students to use in making sense of science phenomena. Teachers wishing to transform instruction with the GRC will discover that reflection on learning is more important than the product of a completed lesson. For students, the GRC is about using practices, core ideas, and crosscutting concepts to reason about the causes of phenomena.

The *Going3DwithGRC* website provides lessons aligned to the standards in the NGSS, and are applicable to three-dimensional science standards aligned to the *Framework*. GRC lessons help teachers to engage students in three-dimensional performances to make sense of phenomena.

Closing Reflections

We hope engaging with this book helps you develop a deeper understanding of three-dimensional science teaching and learning. Using the GRC sequence and lessons in your classroom while reflecting on student learning will help these ideas become part of your vision for teaching. We appreciate and respect your committment to teaching profession and dedication to all students.

References

National Academies of Sciences, Engineering, and Medicine. (2018). *English learners in STEM subjects: Transforming classrooms, schools, and lives.* Washington, DC: The National Academies Press.

National Academies of Sciences, Engineering, and Medicine. (2019). *Science and engineering for grades 6-12: Investigation and design at the center.* Washington, DC: The National Academies Press.

Notes

Notes

Notes

Notes

Printed in the USA
CPSIA information can be obtained
at www.ICGtesting.com
LVHW070059030823
754181LV00011B/183